GERMAN SHORT SEA SHIPPING

by

Bernard and Dominic McCall

FOREWORD

It is important to explain some of the limitations which we imposed on ourselves when compiling this book. The first consideration was the size of ships to be included. The days of the small coaster are almost ended, having been replaced by much larger container feeder vessels which now dominate short-sea routes. As a general rule, we established an upper limit of 4,000 gt but we did allow ourselves some discretion. It may well be that future editions will have to use a still higher limit as the size of ships on feeder services grows still higher.

We have tried to organise the ships within what can best be described as "owning groups". Ship ownership is now a complex multinational business and we have made every effort to unravel this. Readers should be aware that there are various types of "ownership". The registered owner is the company or individual in whose name a ship is legally registered. A subsidiary company is a company in which the majority shareholding is held by a controlling company. An associate company is a company having connections with another because they share some common factor such as a board of directors. A disponent owner is a lessee company which wholly operates a vessel whose registered owner is a leasing or finance company. A manager or managing agent is a company which specifically manages ships for another company under contract or it may manage vessels owned by itself or associated companies. At this point, the situation becomes really complex because management may be operational, commercial or technical - or any combination of these. We hope that we have succeeded in organising the groupings in a way which will be helpful to readers. We have generally avoided phrases such as "managers for . . " or "agents for . . . " because we feel that this would become too complex, even if the information were readily available.

For each ship listed we have given basic details where they are known - figures for some new ships are not always available. It is important to note that, surprisingly, various publications give varying figures. We have used the following sources : Lloyd's Register, Lloyd's Shipping Index, Detlefsens Illustriertes Schiffsregister and information from many of the shipping companies themselves. However, no guarantee is offered about the accuracy of the information. All information is given in good faith and is liable to alteration. Details have been corrected up to 31 July 2001. Readers who have more up-to-date details are invited to contact us.

In addition to the above sources, we wish to acknowledge the help provided by Gil Mayes, Richard Potter, the staff of the Portishead office of Lloyd's Register, all who have supplied photographs, our printers, and the many individuals within the shipping companies listed. Special thanks go to Oliver Sesemann who has checked many details in Germany on our behalf.

Bernard and Dominic McCall

Portishead   September 2001

Published by Bernard McCall, 400 Nore Road, Portishead, Bristol, BS20 8EZ, England.
Telephone/fax : +44 (0)1275 846178. e-mail : bmccall@globalnet.co.uk
All distribution enquries should be addressed to the publisher.

Printed by Sebright Printers,12-18 Stokes Croft, Bristol

ISBN : 1-902953-05-3

JOACHIM ACTUN

CONNIE (ATG)   65   658   749   54.92 9.22   3.21 9.5 gen
(ex Jade-94, Franz Held-82, Mignon-70)

CHRISTIAN F. AHRENKIEL GmbH & CO.

MULTITANK
BAHIA (LBR)   96   3726 5800   99.90 16.50   6.80 15.0 ch tk
MULTITANK
BRACARIA (LBR)   97   3726 5846   99.90 16.50   6.80 15.0 ch tk
MULTITANK
BRASILIA (LBR)   97   3726 5846   99.90 16.50   6.80 15.0 ch tk
   Badenia Shipping Corp.
MULTITANK
BADENIA (LBR)   98   3726 5870   99.90 16.50   6.80 15.0 ch tk
   Partenreederei MT "Multitank Balearia"
MULTITANK
BALEARIA (LBR)   98   3726 5870   99.90 16.50   6.80 15.0 ch tk
   Bolognia Shipping Corp.
MULTITANK
BOLOGNIA (LBR)   97   3726 5846   99.90 16.50   6.80 15.0 ch tk
   Partenreederei m.t. "Multitank Britannia"
MULTITANK
BRITANNIA (DEU) 96   3726 5870   99.90 16.50   6.80 15.0 ch tk
   Partenreederei MT "Multitank Calabria"
MULTITANK
CALABRIA (LBR)   84   2690 4028   91.72 13.59   6.40 12.5 ch tk
   (ex Southern Island-87)
Also larger ships.

GEBRUDER AHRENS KG

   m.s. "Hanna" Gebruder Ahrens KG
HANNA (DEU)   96   3999 5210   101.08 18.45   6.56 15.5 gen(508c)
   m.s. "Rija" Gebruder Ahrens KG
RIJA (DEU)   98   3999 5200   99.95 18.20   6.56 15.5 gen(508c)

ALBATROSS SHIPPING & TRADING GmbH
Transbaltic Shipping Co Inc
KITE (PAN) 69 3585 4995 106.15 15.45 6.74 13.5 tk
(ex Ainazi-96, Aynazhi-91)
Also other ships.

AQUA BLUE BEREEDERUNG GmbH
Racer Shipping Co. Ltd.
AQUA STAR (ATG) 79 1507 1350 67.75 11.74 4.76 12.0 gen(70c)
(ex Susanne L-99, Bremer Mercur-95, Susanne L-89, Bremer Mercur-85, Susanne L-84)

REEDEREI KARL-HEINZ BAASE
J. P. Hauser
BIRKENWALD (ATG) 69 1387 1355 76.31 11.21 3.82 12.0 gen
(ex Henriette Isa-83, Christopher Meeder-75)
Eider Star Navigation Co. Ltd.
EASTWIND (GIB) 76 3006 3844 93.53 14.53 6.05 14.5 gen(210c)
(ex Caribbean Sun-94, Santa Rosa-92, Patricia I-89, Zim Napoli I-88, Trans Luso I-87,
Patricia I-86, Nordic I-85, Zim Napoli-83, Nordic I-83, Zim Northland-83, Nordic-79)
Partenreederei m.s. "Godewind"
GODEWIND (PRT) 77 3622 4450 97.54 16.06 5.72 14.0 gen(343c)
(ex UB Panther-97, Geranta-94, Gracechurch Star-91, Geranta-89, Karen Oltmann-89,
Neerlandia-85, Karen Oltmann-78)
Hans-Peter & Hinrich Hauser
KIEFERNWALD
(DEU) 71 2498 2453 88.52 13.85 5.27 14.0 gen(155c)
(ex Ingeborg II-92, Norrsundet-83, Ursa-77)
Karl-Heinz Baase Schiffahrts KG
OSTWIND (ATG) 79 1624 1610 79.23 13.54 3.53 12.5 gen(142c)
(ex Agila-91, St. Antonius-89, Aros Mistley-86, St Antonius-85)
Partenreederei m.s. "Passatwind"
PASSATWIND (ATG) 77 1889 2159 80.40 12.83 4.87 13.25 gen(128c)
(ex Irina-96, Rugard-95, Veerhaven-92, Rugard-91)
Partenreederei m.s. "Polarwind"
POLARWIND (ATG) 83 3504 3126 97.52 16.03 5.00 13.5 gen(260c)
(ex Freesia-95)
Partenreederei m.s. "Seebrise"
SEEBRISE (ATG) 74 1990 1530 82.15 12.96 4.17 13.5 gen(95c)
(ex Lindaunis-85, Hispania-84, Lindaunis-83, Isle of Man-81, Lindaunis-80)
Partenreederei m.s. "Südwind"
SÜDWIND (ATG) 78 1624 1659 79.23 13.54 3.53 12.5 gen(142c)
(ex Alrek-91, Südwind-89)
Partenreederei m.s. "Westwind"
WESTWIND (ATG) 85 3539 3177 101.02 16.79 5.04 13.5 gen(278c)
(ex Tertia-95)

GÜNTHER BAHR
m.s. "Mignon" Günther Bahr KG
MIGNON (ATG) 66 1069 1220 57.31 10.55 3.92 12.0 gen(44c)
(ex Jana-97, Jan Suhr-81, Siegerland-74)

BALTIC FOREST LINIE GmbH & Co. KG

Baltic Forest Linie m.s. "Baltic Carrier" Schiffahrtsges mbH & Co.

BALTIC CARRIER

        (DEU)   97   2280 3110   82.50 12.50   5.03 11.0 gen(128c)

Baltic Forest Linie m.s. "Baltic Merchant" Schiffahrtsges mbH & Co.

BALTIC MERCHANT

        (DEU)   97   2280 3110   82.50 12.50   4.55 11.0 gen(128c)

Baltic Forest Linie m.s. "Baltic Sailor" Schiffahrtsges mbH & Co.

BALTIC SAILOR

        (DEU)   98   2280 3110   82.50 12.50   4.55 11.0 gen(128c)

Baltic Forest Linie m.s. "Baltic Skipper" Schiffahrtsges mbH & Co.

BALTIC SKIPPER

        (DEU)   97   2280 3110   82.50 12.50   4.55 11.0 gen(128c)

Associated with Pohl Shipping.

The **BALTIC MERCHANT** heads down the River Thames on 17 July 1999 after leaving Tower Wharf at Northfleet. (Kevin Bassett)

J.H. BARR BEFRACHTUNGS- & REEDEREIKONTOR GmbH

J. H. Barr GmbH m.s. "Anita B" KG

ANITA B (TUV)   85   2564 3050   87.91 12.83   4.96 11.0 gen(153c)

    (ex Spica-94)

Ohlrogge Schiffahrts KG

BRAKE (ATG)   57   603   817   57.50 6.54   3.41 9.5 gen

    (ex Marlies-90)

Gottfried Serafin m.s. "Claus" KG

CLAUS (TUV)   87   2006 2723   81.97 12.65   4.52 10.75 gen(104c)

J. H. Barr GmbH & Co. m.s. "Elisia" KG

ELISIA (ATG)   84   1547 1735   82.45 11.38   3.52 10.5 gen(80c)

J. H. Barr GmbH & Co. m.s. "Norderfeld" KG
NORDERFELD (TUV) 96 2345 3992 82.45 12.70 5.31 11.5 gen(162c)
(ex Oyat-98)
Braker Schiffahrtsfonds R. Dittricht & G. Serafin
RUTH-W (TUV) 84 2119 3500 92.11 11.54 5.19 10.75 gen(100c)
J. H. Barr GmbH & Co. m.s. "Sandfeld" KG
SANDFELD (CYP) 84 1547 1735 82.45 11.31 3.52 10.5 gen(48c)
(ex Paloma I-97, Paloma-96, Landkirchen-93)
J. H. Barr GmbH m.s. "Anita Maria" KG
SMÅLAND (TUV) 83 3075 3219 92.41 15.24 4.38 12.0 gen(207c)
(ex Anita Maria-97, Gerd Schepers-94)
J. H. Barr GmbH m.s. "Süderfeld" KG
SÜDERFELD (TUV) 95 2345 3400 82.45 12.70 5.31 11.5 gen(128c)
(ex Pasha-98)

BERND BARTELS
m.s. "Zenit" Bernd Bartels KG
GRACECHURCH CROWN
(ATG) 91 3815 4665 103.50 16.00 6.07 14.5 gen(372c)
(ex Zenit-91)

GERD BARTELS
m.s. "Francop" Gerd Bartels KG
FRANCOP (DEU) 91 3818 4660 103.50 16.24 6.07 14.5 gen(372c)
(ex Aquitaine Spirit-97, CMBT Cutter-96, Emma-96, Rhein Lagan-94, Francop-94,
Manchester Trader-92, Francop-91)
m.s. "Merkur" Reederei G. Bartels KG
MERKUR (DEU) 91 3815 4155 103.50 16.25 6.07 14.5 gen(372c)
Partenreederei m.s. "Nincop"
NINCOP (ATG) 91 3818 4650 103.50 16.24 6.07 14.5 gen(372c)
(ex OPDR Tejo-99, Nincop-95, Norasia Alexandria-95, Nincop-93, City of Valletta-92,
Nincop-91)
Also larger ships.

BAUM & CO.
Partenreederei m.s. "Britta"
BRITTA (ATG) 68 1229 2032 74.02 10.83 5.09 12.5 gen(63c)
(ex Latona-92, Corvus-85, Impala-75)
M. Tensing Schiffahrts-KG m.s. "Jan-Rasmus"
JAN-RASMUS (ATG) 69 1223 2017 74.02 10.83 6.06 13.0 gen(63c)
(ex Arosita-91, John Wulff-76)
**Nordenhamer Bereederungs-gesellschaft mbH (q.v.) is a wholly-owned subsidairy company of
Baum & Co.**

BBC - BURGER BEREEDERUNGS CONTOR GmbH
Reederei m.s. "Anglia" & Co. KG
ANGLIA (CYP) 77 3160 3765 95.28 14.64 5.89 14.5 gen(218c)
(ex Lucy Borchard-91, Baldur-84, Contship Four-79, Baldur-78)
m.s. "Viktoria" Schiffahrtsges. mbH & Co. KG
DANIA (MLT) 85 2691 3036 92.51 13.87 4.12 11.5 gen(166c)
(ex Laica Danielsen-00, Catania Ocean-99, Laica Danielsen-99, MSC Mandala-99,
Mandala-96)

Dithmarsia Schiffahrts KG Danz & Tietjens
DITHMARSIA (ATG) 84 2472 3065 90.02 13.70 4.46 11.5 gen(134c)
(ex P & O Nedlloyd Dover-00, Dithmarsia-98, Zim Colombia-96, Nevis-95, Dithmarsia-90, Azrou-89, Dithmarsia-88)
Danz & Tietjens Schiffahrts KG m.s. "Holsatia"
HOLSATIA (ATG) 85 2472 3050 90.02 13.70 4.43 11.5 gen(134c)
(ex P & O Nedlloyd Calais-00, Point Lisas-99, Lys Carrier-91, Holsatia-89)
Danz & Tietjens Schiffahrts KG m.s. "Siegeria"
OTTAR (DEU) 74 1948 1929 77.45 13.03 3.91 13.5 gen(128c)
(ex Siegeria-90, Siegerland-88, Varberg-84, Siegerland-83)
Also larger ships.

BD SHIPSNAVO GmbH
Partenreederei m.s. "Birgit"
BIRGIT (DEU) 85 1474 1770 77.44 11.41 3.81 11.0 gen
(ex Margit-90, Wesermarsch-88)
Partenreederei m.s. "Katharina II"
KATHARINA D (DEU) 91 2450 3710 87.85 12.81 5.47 11.5 gen(180c)
(ex Emsbroker-00, Katharina D-96)
m.s. "Maria D" Bernhard Dopp Schiffahrts KG
MARIA D (DEU) 86 2370 2760 87.84 12.91 4.45 11.5 gen(144c)

BELUGA SHIPPING GmbH
Blankenese Shipping Co. Ltd.
BLANKENESE (ATG) 84 2882 4200 99.80 14.64 5.33 11.0 gen(174c)
(ex Eembaltic-99, Blankenese-99)
Also larger ships.

With hull proclaiming the identity of her owner, the **BLANKENESE** heads eastwards on the Kiel Canal on 3 September 2000, on passage from Hamburg to St Petersburg. (Dominic McCall)

BERND BECKER KG
m.s. "Jacob Becker" Bernd Becker KG
JACOB BECKER
      (ATG)   95   3999 5315   101.13 18.45   6.56 15.5 gen(508c)
    (ex UB Tiger-97, Jacob Becker-95)

ROLF BECKER
Partenreederei m.s. "Otto Becker"
OTTO BECKER
      (DEU)   89   2749 3144   94.50 16.14   5.00 14.3 gen(262c)

HEINO BEHRMANN
HEINRICH BEHRMANN
      (DEU)   75   2240 2560   81.41 13.64   5.04 13.5 gen(149c)
    (ex Bourgogne-89, Komet I-78, Saracen Prince-76, launched as Komet)

F. H. BERTLING REEDEREI GmbH
KML Lutro Ltd
NERVA (BHS)   75   1259 1395   77.48 10.62   3.58 11.50 gen
    (ex KML Nerva-99, Lutro-99)
KML Rafto Ltd
CARUS (BHS)   69   948 1147   71.18   9.33   3.48 11.0 gen
    (ex KML Carus-99, Rafto-99)
Luena Shipping
COLMAR CASTOR
      (BHS)   85   2173 2583   73.72 13.82   4.21 12.0 gen(140c)
    (ex Luena-99, Kristine-97, Stenheim-87)
Also larger ships.

REEDEREI BRUNO BISCHOFF GmbH & CO.
Bischoff Schiffahrts GmbH & Co. m.s. "Bremer Zukunft" KG
ADMIRAL STAR
      (DEU)   97   2986 4870   98.43 16.90   5.91 15.0 cc(366c)
    (ex Bremer Zukunft-00)
Barney Marine Inc.
BREMER ROLAND
      (NIS)   85   1610 1230   84.03 11.61   3.20 10.75 gen
Bischoff Schiffahrts- GmbH & Co. m.s. "Frigga"
CEC WESER (PMD) 86   3219 4257   100.62 14.30   5.25 12.0 gen(240c)
    (ex Weser-01, Industrial Grace-98, Amke-97, Norbrit Weser-87)
Also larger ships.

KLAUS BLANCK
Bernd Blanck
BETA (DEU)   67   1064 1190   68.43 10.55   3.96 11.0 gen
    (ex Betty-97, Rolf-85)

WILLEM BLANCK
Küstenschiffahrt m.s. "Hela"
HELA (DEU)   66   861 1065   61.75 10.04   3.58 10.5 gen
    (ex Lore-93, Wotan-91)

DIETER BLANKE
m.s. "Warfleth" Blanke Schiffahrts K.G.
WARFLETH (ATG)   80   1022 1092   73.97   9.50   2.88 10.0 gen

WERNER BOCKSTIEGEL BEREEDERUNGS GmbH
W. Bockstiegel GmbH & Co. Reederei KG m.s. "Saar Amsterdam"
A. B. AMSTERDAM
   (ATG)   97   2844 4250   89.90 13.17   5.68 12.0 gen(221c)
 (launched as Saar Amsterdam)
W. Bockstiegel GmbH & Co. Reederei KG m.s. "Saar Bilbao"
A. B. BILBAO (ATG)   97   2844 4212   89.76 13.17   5.68 12.0 gen(221c)
 (launched as Saar Bilbao)

At the end of her voyage from Aveiro to Goole, the **A. B. BILBAO** passes Reedness on the River Ouse on 18 July 1997.   (David H Smith)

W. Bockstiegel GmbH & Co. Reederei KG m.s. "Saar Dublin"
A. B. DUBLIN (ATG) 97   2844 4250   89.90 13.17   5.68 12.0 gen(221c)
 (launched as Saar Dublin)
W. Bockstiegel GmbH & Co. Reederei KG m.s. "Saar Liverpool"
A. B. LIVERPOOL
   (ATG)   96   2844 4250   89.90 13.17   5.68 12.0 gen(237c)
 (ex Saar Liverpool-96)
W. Bockstiegel GmbH & Co. Reederei KG m.s. "A. B. Lübeck"
A. B. LÜBECK (ATG) 97   2844 4250   89.90 13.17   5.68 12.0 gen(221c)
 (launched as Saar Lübeck)
W. Bockstiegel GmbH & Co. Reederei KG m.s. "Saar Valencia"
A. B. VALENCIA
   (ATG)   97   2844 4250   89.90 13.17   5.68 12.0 gen(221c)
 (ex Saar Valencia)

W. Bockstiegel GmbH & Co. Reederei KG m.s. "Canum"
CANUM (ATG)　94　2072　3010　88.30　12.50　　4.55　12.5　gen(154c)
(ex Saar Rouen-96, Canum-95)
W. Bockstiegel GmbH & Co. Reederei KG m.s. "Dornum"
DORNUM (ATG)　93　1682　2369　81.80　11.50　　3.84　10.5　gen(80c)
(ex Saar Madrid-96)
W. Bockstiegel Reederei KG m.s. "Eilsum"
EILSUM (ATG)　91　1662　1920　81.80　11.36　　3.82　10.5　gen(80c)
(ex Saar Lisboa-96)
Enbo Shipping Co. Ltd.
ENNO B (ATG)　83　2649　3525　90.40　14.03　　5.87　14.0　gen(177c)
(ex Torm Assinie-99, Enno B-98, Karin B-98, Marina Heeren-96)
W. Bockstiegel GmbH & Co. Reederei KG m.s. "Freepsum"
FREEPSUM (ATG)　94　1990　3041　88.30　12.50　　4.64　12.5　gen(158c)
(ex Saar Genoa-96)
W. Bockstiegel Reederei GmbH & Co. KG m.s. "Saar London"
GROOTHUSEN
(ATG)　91　1961　2767　88.30　12.76　　4.61　11.4　gen(154c)
(ex Saar London-96)
W. Bockstiegel Reederei KG m.s. "Pilsum"
HEIKO B. (ATG)　93　1662　1970　81.80　11.36　　3.84　10.5　gen(80c)
(ex Pilsum-98, Saar Rotterdam-96)
Werner Bockstiegel GmbH & Co. Reederei KG m.s. "Pewsum"
JENS R (ATG)　90　1960　2960　88.32　12.50　　4.61　11.5　gen(158c)
m.s. "Lea" W. Bockstiegel Reederei GmbH & Co. KG
LEA (ATG)　89　1984　2818　89.30　12.50　　4.33　11.5　gen(150c)
(ex Sonja B-99)
Webo Shipping Co. Ltd.
LYDIA B. (ATG)　91　2497　4173　88.29　13.21　　5.40　12.0　gen(96c)
(ex Venlo-97)
W. Bockstiegel GmbH & Co. Reederei KG m.s. "Malte B"
MALTE B (ATG)　98　2528　3504　84.40　12.80　　5.56　12.0　gen(167c)
(launched as Oldeoog)
Kabo Shipping Co. Ltd.
NILS B (ATG)　98　2528　3506　86.40　12.80　　5.56　12.0　gen(167c)
(launched as Boreas)
Orso Shipping Co. Ltd.
ORSO (ATG)　00　4028　5250　100.55　18.50　　6.47　15.5　gen(519c)
W. Bockstiegel GmbH & Co. Reederei KG m.s. "Osterhusen"
OSTERHUSEN (ATG) 85　1297　1527　74.91　10.60　　3.39　10.0　gen
(ex Jessica S.-94)
W. Bockstiegel Reederei KG m.s. "Rysum"
RYSUM (ATG)　91　1662　2450　81.80　11.36　　4.36　10.5　gen(80c)
(ex Saar Emden-96)
W. Bockstiegel GmbH & Co. Reederei KG m.s. "Sina B"
SINA B (ATG)　85　1298　1537　74.91　12.81　　4.50　10.0　gen
(ex Heike-97, Neil B-96, Sea Tiber-91, Line-91, Webo Liner-86, Neil B-86)
W. Bockstiegel GmbH & Co. Reederei KG m.s. "Suurhusen"
SUURHUSEN (ATG) 96　2805　4256　89.90　13.17　　5.68　11.5　gen(213c)
(ex Saar Roma-96)
W. Bockstiegel GmbH & Co. Reederei KG m.s. "Uphusen"
UPHUSEN (ATG)　96　2846　4334　89.00　13.70　　5.86　11.5　gen(206c)
(ex Saar Bremen-96)

W. Bockstiegel Reederei GmbH & Co. KG m.s. "Saar Antwerp"
UTTUM   (ATG)   93   1662 1935   81.80   11.50   4.35   10.5   gen(80c)
    (ex Saar Antwerp-97)
W. Bockstiegel Reederei GmbH & Co. KG m.s. "Waldtraut B"
WALDTRAUT B
    (ATG)   89   1984 2829   89.30   12.50   4.70   11.0   gen(158c)
W. Bockstiegel GmbH & Co. Reederei KG m.s. "Westerhusen"
WESTERHUSEN
    (ATG)   89   1984 3088   89.31   12.51   4.70   11.5   gen(158c)
    (ex Alpha-99, Bärbel-93)
W. Bockstiegel GmbH & Co. Reederei KG m.s. "Wirdum"
WIRDUM (ATG)   93   2446 3700   87.90   12.89   8.20   10.0   gen(176c)
    (ex Saar Breda-96, Wirdum-93)
W. Bockstiegel GmbH & Co. Reederei KG m.s. "Wolthusen"
WOLTHUSEN   (ATG) 95   2846 4342   90.33   13.20   5.86   11.5   gen(234c)
    (ex Saar Hamburg-96)
Newbuilding:
DEBORAH   (ATG)   01   3900 5100   15.5
Also larger ships.

The **WOLTHUSEN** heads north off the coast of East Anglia on 13 June 1999. She was on
passage from Setubal to Montrose.   (Barry Standerline)

REEDEREI KLAUS BOEHE
Lubeca Shipping Corp.
ALK   (ATG)   77   1801 2623   81.18   11.84   5.11   11.0   gen(91c)
    (ex Talea-00, Anna H-94, Parnass-88)

The **BACCARA** was built at Komarno on the River Danube in Slovakia. She was photographed on 23 July 1998 during her delivery voyage as she passed Anadolu Kavagi on the Bosphorus.

(Oliver Sesemann)

KAPITÄN SIEGFRIED BOJEN SCHIFFAHRTS KG

Bojen m.s. "Baccara" KG
BACCARA (ATG)   98   2997 4433   99.90 12.80   5.68 13.0 gen(297c)
m.s. "Bosporus" Siegfried Bojen KG
BOSPORUS (ATG)   96   2997 4450   99.90 12.80   5.68 13.0 gen(297c)
(ex German Trader-96)
Bojen Schiffahrtsgesellschaft m.s. "Saar Casablanca"
CASABLANCA (ATG) 94   2061 3002   88.54 11.35   4.94 10.5 gen(126c)
(ex Saar Casablanca-97)
Finnhill Shipping Ltd.
HELSINKI (ATG)   97   2810 4245   89.77 13.17   5.72 12.5 gen(229c)
Bojen m.s. "Ibiza" KG
IBIZA (DEU)   01   2997 4450   99.90 12.80   5.68 13.0 gen(297c)
Flowerhill Shipping Ltd.
JACARANDA (ATG) 98   2997 4450   99.90 12.80   5.68 13.0 gen(297c)
Siegfried Bojen m.s. "Heinrich Bojen" KG
JOHANN (ATG)   93   1589 2735   82.56 11.35   4.79 10.5 gen(118c)
(ex Heinrich Bojen-98)
Bojen m.s. "Kopenhagen" KG
KOPENHAGEN
(DEU)   98   2810 4218   89.77 13.17   5.72 12.5 gen(229c)
Bojen m.s. "Korsika" KG
KORSIKA (ATG)   01   2997 4450   99.90 12.80   5.68 13.0 gen(297c)
Bojen m.s. "Mallorca" KG
MALLORCA (DEU) 01   2997 4450   99.90 12.80   5.68 13.0 gen(297c)

Bojen m.s. "Memel" KG
MEMEL   (ATG)   99   2997   4439   99.90   12.80   5.68   13.0   gen(297c)
Siegfried Bojen m.s. "Neermoor" KG
NEERMOOR   (ATG)   93   1589   2735   82.56   11.35   4.79   10.5   gen(118c)
Siegfried Bojen m.s. "Oslo" KG
OSLO   (ATG)   97   2805   4245   89.77   13.17   5.72   12.5   gen(229c)
Letthill Shipping Ltd.
RIGA   (ATG)   98   2810   4245   89.77   13.17   5.72   12.5   gen(229c)
Bojen m.s. "Sardinia" KG
SARDINIA   (ATG)   99   2997   4433   99.90   12.80   5.68   13.0   gen(297c)
Bojen m.s. "Tallin" KG
TALLIN   (ATG)   97   2810   4250   89.77   13.17   5.72   12.5   gen(229c)
m.s. "Taranto" Siegfried Bojen KG
TARANTO   (ATG)   95   2061   3009   88.54   11.35   4.94   10.5   gen(126c)

JOHN HENRY BOLLHORST
Partenreederei m.s. "Stadt Wangen"
STADT WANGEN
   (ATG)   64   934   1112   61.60   10.75   3.81   11.0   gen
(ex Sebastian-87, Steinburg-85, Nordlicht II-76)

ANDREAS & JÜRGEN BÖNING
NEUENBROK   (DEU)   66   409   624   57.41   7.19   2.54   9.5   gen

KLAUS BRAACK GmbH & Co. KG
m.s. "Emja" Braack Schiffahrts KG
EMJA   (ATG)   90   2497   4161   88.29   13.21   5.46   12.0   gen(96c)
m.s. "Delta" Braack Schiffahrts KG
SEABOARD ENDEAVOUR
   (ATG)   98   3862   4974   100.70   16.40   6.24   16.0   gen(406c)
(ex Delta-99)

BRAND-SHIP SERVICE GES. mbH
Cedrela Navigation Co Ltd
ANDRA   (ATG)   83   2605   3235   90.02   14.03   5.58   13.0   gen(177c)
(ex Arnarfell-94, Sandra M-89, Sandra-87, Band Aid III-85, Sandra-85)
Egon Blohm KG m.s. "Atula"
ATULA   (TUV)   86   2006   2723   81.87   12.65   4.52   11.0   gen(104c)
(ex RMS Mercator-96, Atula-94)

BRÖRING OIL TRANSPORT GmbH
ORION   (DEU)   91   356   559   51.50   7.00   2.94   12.5   tk
(ex Ozge Akbasoglu-94)
PEGASUS   (DEU)   65   497   734   59.47   9.35   2.60   8.5   tk
(ex Aqueduct-90, Shell-70)

BRANDARIS BEREEDERUNGSGES. mbH
m.s. "Brandaris" Schiffahrt Brandaris Bereederungs. GmbH & Co. KG
BRANDARIS   (DEU)   85   2007   2460   78.42   12.96   4.46   10.0   gen(133c)

REEDEREI RÖRD BRAREN
Arosia Shipping Ltd.
AROS NEWS (ATG) 85 2816 2923 91.17 13.85 4.36 12.5 gen(187c)
(ex Nioba-97, Bremer Import-91, Nioba-89, Rudolf Karstens-87)
Partenreederei m.s. "Heike Braren"
CELLUS (DEU) 98 4231 6350 99.95 17.00 7.27 15.0 gen(369c)
(launched as Heike Braren)
Partenreederei m.s. "Ute Braren"
FORESTER (DEU) 96 4110 6471 99.99 17.20 7.29 14.0 gen(268c)
(ex Ute Braren-96)
Partenreederei m.s. "Brar Braren"
TIMBUS (DEU) 99 4230 6309 99.98 17.20 7.29 15.5 gen(314c)
(ex Brar Braren-99)

HENRY BREUER KG
Henry Breuer KG m.s. "Paula"
PAULA (DEU) 85 2590 3053 87.99 12.81 5.26 11.5 gen(153c)

HORST BREY
JUTTA-B (DEU) 65 637 740 55.89 8.77 3.06 9.5 gen
(ex Hendrik-87, Doris-75, Gebina-70)

BRIESE SCHIFFAHRTS GmbH & CO. KG
Briese Schiffahrts GmbH & Co KG m.s. "Haaksgat"
ALTA MAR (PMD) 95 2840 4137 89.72 13.60 5.71 13.0 gen(261c)
(ex Senator-96)
Hubertgat Co. Ltd.
BÄRBEL P (GIB) 00 2301 3200 82.50 12.40 5.25 12.2 gen(132c)
(launched as Heinrich G)
Briese Schiffahrts GmbH & Co KG m.s. "Geise"
BAVARIA (DEU) 96 2550 3500 88.00 12.80 5.52 11.5 gen(170c)
Briese Schiffahrts GmbH & Co KG m.s. "Wilgum"
BBC ANGLIA (DEU) 97 4078 4900 100.60 16.60 6.40 15.0 gen(390c)
(ex Industrial Alliance-99, Bremer Forest-97, Wilgum-97)
Briese Schiffahrts GmbH & Co KG m.s. "Hamburger Sand"
BBC AUSTRALIA
(ATG) 90 3236 4595 100.60 14.00 5.75 13.5 gen(240c)
(ex Sina-00, launched as Emma Helene)
Briese Schiffahrts GmbH & Co KG m.s. "Torum"
BBC BRAZIL (DEU) 97 4078 4900 100.60 16.60 6.40 15.5 gen(390c)
(ex Industrial Harmony-00)
Memmert Navigation N.V.
BBC CANADA (ANT) 99 4050 4798 100.60 16.60 6.40 15.0 gen(390c)
(ex Memmert-99)
Briese Schiffahrts GmbH & Co KG m.s. "Wangerooge"
BBC DENMARK
(ANT) 99 4086 4806 100.60 16.60 6.40 15.0 gen(390c)
(launched as Wangerooge)
Briese Schiffahrts GmbH & Co KG m.s. "Leda"
BBC GIBRALTAR
(DEU) 98 2528 3526 85.47 12.80 5.56 12.3 gen(167c)
(ex Bremer Forest-01, Leda-98, launched as Oster Till)

Briese Schiffahrts GmbH & Co KG m.s. "Juister Riff"
BBC JAPAN (ATG) 01 4086 4900 100.62 16.60 6.40 15.5 gen(263c)
(ex Juister Riff-01)
Briese Schiffahrts GmbH & Co KG m.s. "Leysand"
BIENVILLE (ATG) 93 1960 3042 88.30 12.50 4.65 11.5 gen(154c)
(ex Leysand-99)
Briese Schiffahrts GmbH & Co KG m.s. "Rottum"
BREMER FLAGGE
(PMD) 85 3062 3840 99.40 14.15 5.14 12.0 gen(198c)
(ex Santa Helena-97)
Paapsand Shipping Co. Ltd.
BREMER FOREST
(DEU) 00 2532 3390 86.40 12.80 5.56 12.5 gen(167c)
(ex Paapsand-01)
B & B Schiffahrts GmbH & Co. KG m.s. "Bremer Saturn"
BREMER SATURN
(GIB) 94 2854 4045 89.72 13.60 5.72 12.5 gen(172c)
Briese Schiffahrts GmbH & Co KG m.s. "Randzel"
BREMER TIMBER
(DEU) 96 4078 4900 100.60 16.60 6.40 15.0 gen(390c)
(ex Randzel-97)
B & B Schiffahrts GmbH & Co. KG m.s. "Bremer Uranus"
BREMER URANUS
(CYP) 93 2476 3834 85.37 13.32 5.76 13.0 gen(205c)
Briese Schiffahrts GmbH & Co KG m.s. "Ditzum"
DITZUM (ATG) 91 3236 4595 100.60 14.00 5.75 13.5 gen(240c)
(ex Industrial Explorer-99, Mekong Swift-97, Coringle Bay-96, launched as Ditzum)
Briese Schiffahrts GmbH & Co KG m.s. "Dollart"
DOLLART (PMD) 95 2532 3560 88.00 12.80 5.52 11.5 gen(170c)

On 29 May 2001, the **DOLLART** approaches the locks at Holtenau on the outskirts of Kiel during a voyage from Brake to Kaskinen. (Bernard McCall)

Briese Schiffahrts GmbH & Co KG m.s. "Flinthörn"
FLINTHÖRN (ATG) 99 2301 3200 82.50 12.40 5.25 12.2 gen(132c)
Pistoor Schiffahrts GmbH & Co KG m.s. "Freya"
FREYA (PMD) 91 1548 2412 79.63 11.30 5.60 10.0 gen(78c)
Briese Schiffahrts GmbH & Co KG m.s. "Frigga"
FRIGGA (ATG) 87 3230 3938 100.62 14.17 5.21 12.0 gen(240c)
    (ex Sun Bird-96, Ines-93, Sun Bird-93, Ines-92, Deepsea Merchant-88, Sina-88,
    launched as Thule)
Briese Schiffahrts GmbH & Co KG m.s. "Pogum"
HANSE (ATG) 90 1508 1688 79.70 10.90 3.53 10.5 gen(80c)
    (ex Hanse Contor-92, launched as Elena)
Wind Spray Maritime Inc.
HEIMATLAND (VCT) 84 1372 1550 74.98 10.80 3.72 11.0 gen
    (ex Athos-97, Heimatland-96)

Loaded with limestone, the **HEIMATLAND** is ready to depart from Llysfaen Jetty at Llanddulas
on 14 March 2000. (John P Evans)

Briese Schiffahrts GmbH & Co KG m.s. "Helgoland"
INDUSTRIAL ACCORD
    (ANT) 99 4050 4900 100.60 16.60 6.40 15.0 gen(390c)
Rottum Shipping Co. Ltd.
INDUSTRIAL CARIBE
    (ATG) 86 3113 4279 88.60 15.45 6.61 12.5 gen(256c)
    (ex BBC Germany-01, Ranginui-99, Zim Bangkok-94, Anke-93, Global Express 4-89, Anke-88,
    Falcon-88, Anke-87)
Briese Schiffahrts GmbH & Co KG m.s. "Helgoland"
KIMBERLEY (ATG) 97 4453 6900 105.00 16.20 7.53 15.0 gen(320c)
    (ex Helgoland-99)

Briese Schiffahrts GmbH & Co KG m.s. "Kopersand"
KOPERSAND (ATG) 83 1960 3036 88.30 12.50 4.65 10.5 gen(158c)
Bremer Reederei Eilemann & Bischoff GmbH
MARSCHENLAND
      (ATG) 85 1373 1550 74.98 10.80 3.70 11.0 gen
Briese Schiffahrts GmbH & Co KG m.s. "Bingumer Sand"
MIRAMAR (DEU) 96 2840 4135 89.73 13.60 5.71 13.0 gen(261c)
(ex Bingumersand-97, Geestborg-96)
Briese Schiffahrts GmbH & Co KG m.s. "Hohe Horn"
MUSKETIER (PMD) 97 2840 4128 89.72 13.60 5.71 13.0 gen(261c)
Briese Schiffahrts & Co. KG m.s. "Nesserland"
NESSERLAND (GIB) 93 2825 4148 89.90 13.44 5.60 11.5 gen
(ex Swift-00)
Briese Tonnagesteuer Fonds GmbH
NEUWERK (GIB) 00 2545 3604 86.40 12.80 5.52 11.3 gen(170c)
(ex Eemcarib-00)
Parameter Navigation S.A.
PORTHOS (VCT) 77 2351 2378 86.52 13.03 4.86 12.5 gen(162c)
(ex Thor-96, Flensburger Flagge-95, Bremer Flagge-95, Schwinge-77)
Briese Schiffahrts GmbH & Co KG m.s. "Dyksterhusen"
PROGRESO (ATG) 91 1960 3053 88.30 12.50 4.64 11.4 gen(154c)
(ex Franz Keller-99, launched as Tima Jupiter)
Briese Schiffahrts GmbH & Co KG m.s. "Odin"
S. GABRIEL (DEU) 97 4078 4900 100.60 16.60 6.40 15.0 gen(360c)
(ex Industrial Unity-99, Odin-98, Industrial Unity-99, Odin-98)
Briese Schiffahrts GmbH & Co KG m.s. "Janssand"
SANTIAGO (DEU) 97 2528 3529 88.60 12.80 5.52 12.3 gen(167c)
(ex Janssand-97)
Briese Schiffahrts GmbH & Co KG m.s. "Saxum"
SAXUM (GIB) 00 2301 3200 82.50 12.40 5.25 12.2 gen(132c)
(launched as Gerhard G)
Briese Schiffahrts GmbH & Co KG m.s. "Scharhörn"
SCHARHÖRN (GIB) 00 2301 3200 82.50 12.40 5.25 12.2 gen(132c)
Briese Schiffahrts GmbH & Co KG m.s. "Ems"
SEA MERSEY (ATG) 90 1552 2399 79.62 11.30 4.42 10.0 gen(24c)
(Remmer-00)
Briese Schiffahrts GmbH & Co KG m.s. "Athene"
STAR (PMD) 91 2237 2700 82.50 12.62 4.69 11.5 gen(138c)
(launched as Huberna)
Briese Schiffahrts GmbH & Co KG m.s. "Störtebeker"
STÖRTEBEKER
      (GIB) 00 2301 3200 82.50 12.40 5.25 12.2 gen(132c)
Briese Schiffahrts GmbH & Co KG m.s. "Midumer Sand"
TORNATOR (PMD) 95 2840 4178 89.72 13.70 5.71 13.0 gen(261c)
Briese Schiffahrts GmbH & Co KG m.s. "Jemgumer Sand"
VENTURE (ATG) 94 2446 3717 87.90 12.80 5.50 12.0 gen(176c)
(ex Sea Severn-01, Venture-00, MSC Venture-99, Lys Trader-96)
Briese Schiffahrts KG m.s. "Wilke" GmbH
WILKE (CYP) 94 2901 4223 91.09 13.80 5.75 13.5 gen(232c)
(ex Leknes-99)
Also larger ships.

BRISE SCHIFFAHRTS GmbH

Cembreze Shipping Co Ltd
BALTRADER (ATG) 71 1181 1745 69.19 11.31 5.36 11.5 cem
(ex Arguineguin Uno-86, Uralar-75)

Boxter Shipping Co. Ltd.
BOXTER (CYP) 81 2023 2840 79.71 13.03 5.68 12.0 gen(144c)
(ex Baltic Bridge-97, Eliza Heeren-95, Akak Success-86, Eliza Heeren-86)

Coral Sea Shipping Ltd.
CEMSEA (ATG) 79 2657 3885 82.52 14.36 6.10 13.25 cem
(ex Coral Sea-95, Coral-91, Puerto De Aguilas-83, Duro Seis-82)

Forester Shipping Co. Ltd.
FORESTER (ATG) 90 2827 4261 88.20 13.68 5.79 11.0 gen(173c)
(ex Arklow Viking-99)

Sunset Shipping Co. Ltd.
LARK (ATG) 76 1972 2463 79.02 12.43 4.77 11.5 gen(104c)
(ex Hoogen-94, Aland-83)
SWALLOW (ATG) 77 1968 2052 79.20 12.43 4.78 12.0 gen(100c)
(ex Hinden-94, Värmland II-87, Värmland-83)

Shark Shipping Co. N.V.
MARGARETA (ANT) 84 1850 2550 83.19 11.46 4.40 10.5 cem

Solarhav Shipping Co. Ltd
SOLAR (ATG) 77 2361 2680 86.52 13.03 5.20 12.5 gen(140c)
(ex Marburg-92, Solar-85)

Reederei m.s. "Sunnanhav"
SUNNANHAV (ATG) 77 2351 2350 86.52 13.03 4.86 12.5 gen(140c)

Cembra Shipping Co. Ltd.
SVENDBORG (ATG) 84 2730 2931 98.30 13.52 4.25 10.5 gen(157c)
(ex Navaro-93)

Thruster Shipping Co. Ltd.
THRUSTER (ATG) 90 2827 4261 88.20 13.68 5.79 11.0 gen(173c)
(ex Arklow Venture-00)

Vänerhav Shipping Co. Ltd.
VÄNERLAND (ATG) 77 2351 2669 86.52 13.03 5.20 12.25 gen(140c)
(ex Vänerhav-96, Rebena-96)

G. BUCK SCHIFFAHRTS KG

G. Buck Schiffahrts KG m.s. "Figaros"
FIGAROS (ATG) 80 2050 3254 80.32 13.85 6.56 13.5 gen(132c)
(ex Unamar-92, Figaros-89)

m.v. "Lady Bos" Shipping Co.
LADY BOS (IOM) 79 2141 3300 80.32 13.85 6.56 13.5 gen(132c)

REEDEREIVERWALTUNG WILFRIED BUCK

m.s. "Laila" Buck Schiffahrts KG
LAILA (ATG) 83 2837 2352 91.01 13.54 4.60 10.5 gen/ro(158c)

Melora Marine Co. Ltd,
LINDA BUCK (CYP) 85 2295 2584 95.92 14.23 4.07 10.0 gen/ro(180c)
(ex Britannia-96, RMS Britannia-93, Linda Buck-93)

Ophelia Shipping Co. Ltd.
ROLF BUCK (CYP) 85 2295 2591 95.92 14.23 4.07 10.0 gen/ro(180c)

HERMANN BUSS GmbH & CIE.

Vierunddreissigste Grosse Bleichen Schiffahrtsges mbH & Co. KG

BARTEN	(ATG)	98	3239	4803	96.00	13.60	6.13	12.5	gen(216c)

Harvest Libra Navigation Co. Ltd.

BORNEO	(CYP)	97	2919	4477	88.20	13.60	6.12	12.0	gen(176c)

Pan Reefer Co. Ltd.

EDDA	(CYP)	85	2729	2812	99.33	13.52	4.50	11.5	gen(137c)

(ex Torm Tema-98, Edda-97)

Hermann Buss KG m.s. "Frieda" GmbH & Co.

FRIEDA	(ATG)	96	2901	4515	88.20	13.66	6.19	10.5	gen(198c)

The Leer-registered **FRIEDA** was photographed in the Bristol Channel as she approached Newport on 20 July 1997. (Danny Lynch)

Iron Head Shipping Co. Ltd.

HUEMMLING	(CYP)	85	2730	2947	98.30	13.59	4.27	10.5	gen(157c)

(ex Belida-96, Helena I-96, Almaris-94)

Vierstigste Grosse Bleichen Schiffahrtsges mbH & Co. KG

JONAS	(ATG)	85	2729	2814	98.33	13.52	4.50	11.5	gen(157c)

(ex Pegwell Bay-98, Altair-85)

Drieundvierzigste Grosse Bleichen Schiffahrtsges mbH & Co. KG

NOORT	(ATG)	89	910	1086	69.10	9.50	3.00	9.0	gen(56c)

Hermann Buss KG m.s. "Northsea Trader" GmbH & Co.

NORTHSEA TRADER

	(ATG)	95	4984	6974	116.40	19.50	7.06	16.0	cc(532c)

(ex Gracechurch Comet-99, Northsea Trader-97, Texel Bay-96, Northsea Trader-95)

Cymoon Shipping Co. Ltd.

OLIVIA	(CYP)	78	1990	3050	80.68	14.33	5.11	12.5	gen

(ex Fjord Star-95, Caroline-93, Cindy-89, Altappen-86)

Hermann Buss KG m.s. "Ruth" Gmbh & Co.

RUTH	(ATG)	91	2873	4557	88.20	13.68	6.11	11.0	gen(173c)

Zweiundvierzigste Grosse Bleichen Schiffahrtsges mbH & Co. KG
TRANSPORTÖR
      (DEU)   90   2875 4566   88.20 13.68   6.11 11.0 gen(173c)
Hermann Buss KG m.s. "Western Trader" Gmbh & Co.
WESTERN TRADER
      (ATG)   91   4164 4744 111.10 16.07   5.94 14.5 gen(381c)
    (ex Gracechurch Meteor-97, launched as Western Trader)
Also larger ships.

REEDEREI JOHANNA CLAUSSEN KG
m.s. "Anne Catharina" Reederei-Ges. Johanna Claussen KG
ANNE CATHARINA
      (ATG)   86   3147 3324   90.02 15.52   4.71 12.5 gen(276c)
    (ex Georgetown-87, Anne Catharina-86)
Schiffahrtsgesellschaft J. Claussen KG
CHRISTOPHER MEEDER
      (ATG)   76   2154 2200   86.92 12.98   4.75 13.0 gen(135c)

REEDEREI HEINZ CORLEIS KG
KATRIN (DEU)   86   3448 4250 101.45 15.24   3.80 12.5 gen(134c)
    (launched as Odin)
Also larger ships.

CUXHAVENER MINERALöL GmbH
ANITA (DEU)   65   149   237   35.34 6.33   2.03 8.7 tk
CORA (DEU)   69   169   264   38.23 6.53   1.97 9.0 tk
    (ex Kurt-86)
EBBA (DEU)   68   248   396   44.96 6.84   2.44 11.0 tk
    (ex Emstank 14-78)
FINJA (DEU)   00   942 1137   64.91 10.00   3.70 11.0 tk
These vessels are managed by Glüsing Transport GmbH (q.v.)

WILLI DADE
FRANKO (DEU)   65   342   480   47.99 7.22   2.54 11.0 gen

REEDEREI FRANK DAHL
DANIO (ATG)   01   1499 1805   80.90 11.42   3.20 10.0 gen
REMORA (ATG)   00   1499 1805   80.90 11.42   3.20 10.0 gen
    Partenreederei m.s. "Denika"
DENIKA (ATG)   78   1495 1550   76.84 11.49   3.39 11.0 gen(62c)
    (ex Sea Merlan-98, launched as Merlan)
    Reederei Frank Dahl m.s. "Graneborg" GmbH & Co. KG
GRANEBORG (DEU) 97   2863 4113   89.72 13.60   5.72 13.0 gen(261c)
    Partenreederei m.s. "Magula"
MAGULA (ATG)   80   1655 1548   82.96 11.40   3.17 11.0 gen(72c)
    (ex Sea Magula-98)
    Reederei Frank Dahl m.s. "Orade" KG
ORADE (DEU)   90   1354 1699   77.00 11.40   3.17 10.5 gen(94c)
    (ex Sea Orade-98, launched as Orade)
Also the larger VEERSEBORG.

FRIEDHELM DEDE KG
m.s. "Inke Dede" Friedhelm Dede KG
GRACECHURCH COMET
    (ATG)   92   5006 6580   116.73 18.15   6.86 16.0 cc(510c)
    (ex Inka Dede-01, Armada Sprinter-96, Inka Dede-95, Rhein Liffey-94, Inka Dede-93)
m.s. "Sven Dede" Friedhelm Dede KG
GRACECHURCH HARP
    (ATG)   91   3815 4659   103.50 16.00   6.07 14.5 gen(372c)
    (launched as Sven Dede)

PETER DÖHLE SCHIFFAHRTS-KG (GmbH & CO.)
Partenreederei m.s. "Christa Kerstin" Uwe Jager
CHRISTA KERSTIN
    (ATG)   82   1939 2890   87.97 11.33   4.68 11.5 gen(90c)
    (ex Esteburg-90, Bilbao-89, Sea Este-86, Esteburg-83)
m.s. "Cosmea" Christian Trost Schiffahrts-Gesellschaft KG
COSMEA (DEU)   90   1985 2620   82.50 12.50   4.47 11.0 gen(96c)
m.s. "Doris T" Schiffahrtsgesellschaft mbH & Co.
DORIS T. (ATG)   77   1973 2150   79.00 12.43   4.77 12.0 gen(104c)
    (ex Libra II-97, Libra-85)
Globehelier Maritime Ltd
HAJO (ATG)   83   3780 4646   96.98 17.63   5.96 14.25 gen(356c)
    (ex Takitimu-98, Ocean-94, Velazquez-91, Ocean-88, City of Salerno-87, Ocean-86,
    Akak Ocean-86, Ocean-84)
Partenreederei m.s. "Xandrina"
XANDRINA (ATG)   86   1567 1750   81.21 11.38   3.44 9.75 gen(72c)
Also larger ships.

KAPITÄN MANFRED DRAXL SCHIFFAHRTS GmbH
Zenit Schiffahrtgesellschaft mbh & Co. m.s. "Anne"
ANNE (ATG)   80   1588 1604   79.71 11.41   3.34 10.75 gen
    (ex Anda-91)
Kapitän Manfred Draxl Bereederungs GmbH & Co. KG m.s. "Antina"
ANTINA (DEU)   89   2292 2750   80.16 12.80   4.43 11.0 gen(125c)
Schiffahrtgesellschaft Nord GmbH & Co. KG m.s. "Assiduus"
ASSIDUUS (ATG)   90   2292 2727   84.90 12.80   4.43 11.0 gen(137c)
    (ex Lehship-90, Assiduus-90)
Condra Schiffahrts GmbH & Co. m.s. "Balmung"
BALMUNG (DEU)   91   2326 2752   84.90 12.92   4.27 11.0 gen(157c)
    (ex Panda II-99, launched as Edith)
Kapitän Manfred Draxl Schiffahrts GmbH & Co. KG m.s. "Elisabeth"
ELISABETH (DEU)   93   3958 5350   107.98 16.40   6.00 16.0 cc(448c)
Kapitän Manfred Draxl KG m.s. "Marman"
MARMAN (ATG)   85   1782 2507   83.19 11.46   4.40 10.5 gen(72c
Kapitän Manfred Draxl Schiffahrts GmbH & Co. KG m.s. "Dörte"
MATHILDA (ATG)   94   3957 5388   107.98 16.40   5.99 16.0 cc(448c)
    (ex Dörte-94)
Esdra Schiffahrts GmbH & Co. KG m.s. "Miriam"
MIRIAM (DEU)   98   4163 5055   99.95 16.20   6.39 14.75 gen(374c)
Condra Schiffahrts GmbH & Co. KG m.s. "Asgard"
RIVER ALN (ATG)   00   2858 4850   89.80 13.60   6.40 12.0 gen(183c)
    (launched as Asgard)

Condra Schiffahrts GmbH & Co. KG m.s. "Baldur"
RIVER BLYTH (ATG) 00   2858 4850   89.80 13.60   6.40 12.0 gen(183c)
(launched as Baldur)
Condra Schiffahrts GmbH & Co. KG m.s. "Thor"
RIVER TYNE (ATG) 99   2858 4850   89.80 13.60   6.40 12.0 gen(183c)
(launched as Thor)
Also larger ships.

The **RIVER BLYTH** arrives at Immingham from Sluiskil on 3 September 2000. Along with the **RIVER ALN** and **RIVER TYNE**, she is on charter to the British company Stephenson Clarke.

(David Dixon, courtesy ABP Immingham)

REEDEREI HANS-PETER ECKHOFF GmbH & Co. KG
m.s. "Magnolia" Reederei Hans Eckhoff KG
DEVER (ATG)   83   2768 2848   96.51 13.67   4.33 11.5 gen(257c)
(ex Magnus E-98, Veerhaven-91, Magnus E-90)
m.s. "Kamilla" Reederei Hans-Peter Eckhoff GmbH & Co. KG
KAMILLA (ATG)   85   2740 2785   98.30 13.59   5.31 11.5 gen(169c)
m.s. "Nunki" Reederei H. P. Eckhoff GmbH & Co. KG
LYS CARRIER (ATG) 94   2446 3726   87.90 12.89   5.16 11.5 gen(176c)
(ex Nunki-94)
m.s. "Ile de France" GmbH & Co KG
SKAGEN (ATG)   99   2545 3490   86.40 12.80   5.55 11.4 gen(167c)
(launched as Ile de France)

EGGERS SCHIFFAHRTS KG
Ariane Shipping Co. Ltd.
TRANSPORT (ATG) 71   1919 1750   74.71 13.03   4.26 13.0 gen(102c)
(ex Crioula-00, Ariane-97, Ariane I-90, Slano-87, Scan Glen-86, Biscayne Sky-82, Sligo-78)

HEINZ EHLER
m.s. "Katharina Ehler" Schiffsbetriebs gesellschaft mbH & Co. KG
KATHARINA EHLER
        (DEU)   93   3992 5335   99.95 18.44   6.56 15.5 gen(515c)
Also the larger ANKE EHLER and MONIKA EHLER.

EICKE SCHIFFAHRTS KG
"Carol Ann" Eicke Schiffahrts KG
CAROL ANN (ATG)   94   3992 5331   99.95 18.44   6.56 16.0 cc(509c)
"Emily" Eicke Schiffahrts KG
EMILY (ATG)   90   2190 3238   82.50 12.62   5.29 10.5 gen(138c)
Also the larger MARY ANN.

KLAUS EILBRECHT SCHIFFAHRTS KG
Klaus Eilbrecht Schiffahrts KG m.s. "Elke"
ELKE (ATG)   84   1299 1537   74.91 10.60   3.20 10.0 gen
     (ex Mareike B-94, Sea Tagus-91, Webo Carrier-86, Mareike B-86)
Klaus Eilbrecht Schiffahrts KG m.s. "Jan-Willem"
JAN-WILLEM (DEU) 86   1525 1505   74.33 12.45   3.60 10.0 gen(84c)
Klaus Eilbrecht Schiffahrts GmbH & Co. KG m.s. "Westerems"
SEA CLYDE (DEU)   84   1843 2348   80.07 12.70   4.17 11.0 gen(102c)
     (ex Petena-97)
Eilbrecht Schiffahrts GmbH & Co. KG m.s. "Tomke"
TOMKE (GIB)   00   2301 3200   82.50 12.60   5.25 12.0 gen(132c)

ELBE TRANS SCHIFFAHRTS GmbH
m.s. "Algol" Elbe Trans Schiffahrts GmbH & Co. KG
ALGOL (ATG)   95   1864 2580   82.38 11.45   4.79 12.0 gen(105c)
     (ex RMS Algol-98)
m.s. "Antares" Elbe Trans Schiffahrts GmbH & Co. KG
ANTARES (ATG)   95   1298 1537   74.91 10.60   4.79 12.8 gen(105c)
     (ex RMS Antares-99, Antares-95)
Aries Shipping Co Ltd
ARIES (ATG)   97   2456 3660   87.90 12.89   5.49 11.5 gen(176c)
     (ex RMS Aries-01, Aries-97)
m.s. "Atair" Elbe Trans Schiffahrts GmbH & Co. KG
ATAIR (ATG)   95   1864 2489   82.38 11.46   4.79 12.8 gen(105c)
     (ex RMS Atair-98, Atair-96)
Castor Shipping Co Ltd
AURIGA (ATG)   96   2460 3715   87.90 12.89   4.79 11.5 gen(176c)
     (ex Wani Auriga-01, Auriga-00, RMS Auriga-99, Auriga-96)
m.s. "Apollo" Elbe Trans Schiffahrts GmbH & Co. KG
LYS CLIPPER (ATG) 94   2446 3706   87.90 12.89   5.16 11.5 gen(176c)
     (ex Apollo-95)
Aldebaran Shipping Co Ltd
RMS ALDEBARAN
        (ATG)   96   1864 2516   85.20 11.35   4.79 12.0 gen(105c)
     (launched as Aldebaran)
Andromeda Shipping Co Ltd
RMS ANDROMEDA
        (ATG)   97   1864 2516   82.50 11.45   4.79 12.8 gen(105c)
     (launched as Andromeda)

Arctur Shipping Co Ltd
RMS ARCTURUS
        (DEU)   96   1864 2517   82.35 11.45   4.79 12.8 gen(105c)
(ex Arcturus-96)
Associated with Rohden Bereederung GmbH & Co. KG

EMSTANK GmbH
EMSTANK 7 (DEU) 63   104   248   34.02   5.72   1.85 10.0 tk
EMSTANK 10 (DEU) 66   152   236   34.98   6.51   2.07 10.5 tk

ERKA-SHIPPING GmbH
Troubador Shipping Co Ltd
ERKA SUN (ATG) 79 4012 4352   104.15 16.77   5.65 14.5 cc(300c)
(ex CTE Tarragona-01, Erka Sun-00, Sinar Bandung-99, Erka Sun-98, City of Lisbon-88, City of Perth-85)
Also larger vessels

TANKREEDEREI FEHNER GmbH
Partenreederei m.s. "Bernd" Tankreederei Fehner GmbH
BERND (DEU)   67   607   993   65.69   8.34   3.51 11.0 tk

FELDMANN SCHIFFSERVICE GmbH
BITUNAMEL III
        (DEU)   53   101   168   29.14   5.22   1.90 10.0 tk
(ex Shell 53-64, Carlsson II-53)

REEDEREI R. FISCHER VERWALTUNGSGESELLSCHAFT mbH
Reederei m.s. "Borstel" R. Fischer GmbH & Co. KG
ATLANTIK (ATG)   93 4193 5401   111.10 16.19   6.55 16.0 gen(417c)
(ex Birgit Jurgens-98)

UWE FISCHER KG
m.s. "Andrina F." Schiffahrtsgesellschaft Uwe Fischer KG
ANDRINA F. (ATG) 90 1568 1890   81.20 11.30   3.66   9.5 gen(72c)
(ex Simone-92)
m.s. "Petra F." Uwe Fischer KG
PETRA F. (ATG) 85 1567 1976   81.21 11.33   3.72   9.7 gen(72c)

FISSER & VAN DOORNUM
Androlikou Shipping Co. Ltd.
ANGUS (CYP)   76 1989 2767   79.05 12.43   4.77 12.0 gen(104c)
(ex Andros-93, Alsterberg-86)
Antigua Shipping Co. Ltd.
ANTIGUA (CYP)   81 3253 4613   98.69 15.52   6.01 14.0 ch tk
Bonaire Navigation Co. Ltd.
BONAIRE (CYP)   82 3253 4563   98.89 15.52   6.01 14.0 ch tk
Clonakilty Shipping Ltd.
CAMIRA (IRL)   97 4107 5216   100.62 16.20   6.40 15.5 gen(374c)
Emerald Isle Containers Ltd.
CONNEMARA (IRL) 98 4095 5216   99.95 16.20   6.40 15.5 gen(373c)
Teal Bay Shipping & Co. Ltd.
CORONA (CYP)   98 4150 5184   99.95 16.20   6.40 14.5 gen(374c)

Criterion Marine Co. Ltd.
COSA   (CYP)   72   4255 6370   101.48   16.01   7.22 13.0 bulk(203c)
(ex Ventus-85, Erika Fisser-79)
Draughtsman Shipping Co. Ltd.
DRAX   (CYP)   77   2205 3927   82.50   13.37   6.56 9.2 gen
(ex Drau-91, Santana-81, Santa Teresa-81)
Innocuous Shipping Co. Ltd.
INNES   (CYP)   76   4372 6300   106.61   16.64   6.75 12.0 gen(206c)
(ex Conticarib-96, Innes-94, Inn-92, Ventus-79, Josun-78)
Alasce Shipping Co. Ltd.
KELLS   (CYP)   77   1986 2655   79.20   12.43   4.77 10.5 gen(104c)
(ex Götaland-88)
Emerald Isle Bulkers Ltd.
KILLARNEY   (IRL)   77   2501 2908   96.25   12.43   4.77 12.0 gen(207c)
(ex Anholt-86, Neuwerk-81)
KYLEMORE   (ATG)   77   2563 2908   96.32   12.43   4.73 10.5 gen(207c)
(ex Borssum-95, Bregenz-92, Bornholm-86, Neukloster-81)
Zachariassen Schiffahrtsgesellschaft mbH & Co. KG
KRONOBORG   (CYP) 98 4128 5216 100.62   16.20   6.40 15.5 gen(374c)
Hans-Christoph Gassan
MARILENA   (ATG)   69   1217 1975   74.53   10.83   5.06 12.5 gen(90c)
(ex Mariam-00, Euro Clipper-97, Destel-80, Owen Kersten-77, Destel-73)
Melissa Shipping Co. Ltd.
MELISSA   (CYP)   77   1989 2772   79.13   12.43   5.42 12.0 gen(104c)
(ex Messberg-86)

The **MELISSA** is a member of a standard class of coastal ships built in Japan in the late 1970s.
She is seen leaving the locks at IJmuiden to head up the North Sea Canal towards Amsterdam
on 20 April 2001.   (Dominic McCall)

Murray Shipping Co. Ltd.
MURRAY (CYP)   77   2201 3963   82.23   13.37   6.46   9.2 gen
(ex Mur-91, Agate Prosperity-82, Atlantic Prosperity-81, Danship-77, launched as
Frendo Danship)
Okapi Shipping Co. Ltd
OKAPI (CYP)   72   4255 6329   101.48   16.03   7.22 13.0 bulk(203c)
(ex Tabla-86, Boca Tabla-82, Imela Fisser-73)
Pyrgos Marine Co. Ltd.
PYRGOS (CYP)   72   4255 6329   101.48   16.01   7.22 13.0 bulk(203c)
(ex Villiers-86, Elisabeth Fisser-79)
Salamander Shipping Co. Ltd.
SALAMANDER (CYP) 74   2197 4005   82.23   13.37   6.49   9.2 gen(129c)
(ex Salzach-91, Hilary M.-83, Hilary Weston-83, Frendo Hope-76)
Sterakovou Shipping Co. Ltd.
STERAKOVOU (CYP) 74   2197 4006   82.23   13.37   6.49   9.2 gen(129c)
(ex Steyr-91, Monitor-82, Caroline Weston-82, Frendo Grace-76)
Zachariassen & Fisser Schiffahrtsges. mbH & Co. KG
WASABORG (CYP)   97   4107 5216   100.62   16.20   6.40 15.5 gen(374c)
(ex P & O Nedlloyd Belem-98, Wasaborg-98)

HEIYO FUNCK
Chantal Shipping Co. Ltd.
SIAN (ATG)   75   1547 2723   73.41   11.82   5.51   gen
(ex Ilse-00, Sian-97, Irina-91, Coenraad Kuhlman-86)

On 19 June 2000, the **SIAN** was photographed as she passed Walsoorden on her way up the
River Scheldt to Antwerp.   (Tony Hogwood)

HANS OTTO GADERMANN
Rumpus Shipping Co Ltd

MIKA (CYP) 71 1895 2366 77.96 12.83 5.50 12.25 gen
   (ex Luna-92, Lona-88, Janica-88, Euro Freighter-87, Maria Graebe-83, Kungsbron-73, launched as Maria Graebe)

GEFO GESELLSCHAFT FÜR ÖLTRANSPORTE mbH & CO.

DONIZETTI (LUX) 00 2335 3614 93.60 12.50 4.65 13.0 ch tk
VERDI (ATG) 99 2195 3079 93.60 12.50 4.65 13.0 ch tk
   Hansa Befrachtungs GmbH
BELLINI (ATG) 99 2195 3046 93.60 12.50 4.65 13.0 ch tk
MOZART (ATG) 00 2195 3048 93.60 12.50 4.65 13.0 ch tk
   Oceanflag Shipping Ltd.
PUCCINI (CYP) 98 2195 3052 93.60 12.50 4.65 13.0 ch tk
ROSSINI (CYP) 98 2195 3090 93.60 12.50 4.65 13.0 ch tk

HENRY GERDAU KG GmbH & Co.
Reedereiges. m.s. "Komet" Henry Gerdau KG GmbH & Co.

KOMET III (DEU) 90 4169 4752 111.10 16.07 5.98 15.3 gen(378c)
   (ex Portugal Bridge-97, Komet III-96, Gracechurch Comet-96, Komet III-91)
PLANET V (DEU) 94 4984 7014 116.40 19.50 7.06 16.5 gen(532c)
   (ex Gracechurch Planet-97, Planet V-96)

GERDES SCHIFFAHRTS GmbH &Co. KG
Kapitän Josef Gerdes Schiffahrtsges mbH KG m.s. "Ajos G"

AJOS G (DEU) 96 2061 3000 88.45 11.35 4.95 10.5 gen(118c)
   Kapitän Josef Gerdes Schiffahrtsgesellschaft mbH KG m.s. "Annlen G"
ANNLEN G (ATG) 95 2061 3004 88.45 11.35 4.95 11.5 gen(118c)
   (ex Duisburg-96, Annlen-G-95)
   Gerems Schiffahrts GmbH & Co. KG m.s. "Gerhein G"
GERHEIN G (ATG) 88 910 1085 69.10 9.46 3.00 10.5 gen(36c)
   (ex Karina G-98, Sea Douro-96, launched as Leda)
   Gerems Schiffahrts GmbH & Co. KG m.s. "Nikar G"
NIKAR G (ATG) 00 2335 3200 82.50 12.40 5.25 12.2 gen(132c)
   Kapitän Josef Gerdes Schiffahrtsgesellschaft mbH KG m.s. "Nicole G"
PIA (DEU) 87 2236 2850 82.30 12.58 4.88 11.5 gen(153c)
   Kapt. J. Gerdes Schiffahrts GmbH KG m.s. "Heinger G"
TANJA (PMD) 89 2190 2735 82.50 12.60 4.71 11.0 gen(138c)

BERNHARD GERDES

GERLENE (DEU) 62 217 372 40.77 7.14 2.19 7.0 gen
   (ex Hertraud-88)

GERMAN TANKER SHIPPING GmbH & Co. KG
t.m.s. "Hai"

HAI (DEU) 81 2025 3150 86.70 12.53 5.67 12.5 tk
Also larger ships.

HANS-PETER GEWANDT
Black Lion shipping Co. Ltd.

INGRID (CYP) 90 1960 2803 89.30 12.50 4.61 10.5 gen(158c)

H. GLAHR & CO. GmbH & CO. KG
North Transit Marine Inc.
BALTIC CHAMP
      (PAN)   77   1660 2060   71.96   12.81   4.45 12.0 gen(127c)
    (ex Pico Ruivo-95, Nordlicht II-83)
Courier Baltic Container Carriers (Marine) Ltd.
BALTIC COURIER
      (CYP)   77   1667 2060   71.96   12.83   4.45 12.0 gen(132c)
    (ex Jörn Dede-95, Akak Progress-86, Jörn Dede-83, Bell Valiant-78, launched as Jörn Dede)
Also larger ships.

GLÜSING TRANSPORT GmbH
Reederei Glüsing & Co.
GUDRUN (DEU)   82   676   809   58.22   10.11   3.10 10.5 tk
    m.t. "Heide" Reederei Glusing KG
HEIDE (DEU)   86   672   801   58.02   10.04   3.06 10.5 ch tk
    Partenreederei m.s. "Merle"
MERLE (DEU)   80   510   593   49.81   9.22   2.85 10.5 tk
This company manages the tankers of Cuxenhavener Mineralöl Gmbh (q.v.)

HORST GÜNTHER GÖBEL
Partenreederei m.s. "Lys-Bris"
VIRGO (ATG)   78   2361 2369   86.50   13.03   4.86 13.5 gen(140c)
    (ex Lys-Bris-98, Virgo-89)

GERD GÖRKE
CORINNA (ATG)   74   2130 2450   81.41   13.44   4.89 13.7 gen(144c)
    (ex Vantage-93, Bell Vantage-78)
LUCAS (VCT)   84   2472 3065   90.02   13.70   4.61 11.5 gen(134c)
    (ex Oriental Dragon-98, Sonja-95, Martini-94, Paul-92, Tiger Wave-90, Paul-89, Band Aid I-86, Paul-85)
TINKA (ATG)   76   2219 2560   81.41   13.47   5.03 13.7 gen(150c)
    (ex Taras-96, Ikaria-86)
    m.s. "Marianne" Schiffahrtsges. mbH
MARIANNE (ATG)   74   2765 3318   93.20   14.53   5.51 14.5 gen(202c)
    (ex OPDR Cartagena-98, Casablanca-97, Francop-90, Manchester Faith-83, Francop-83, Manchester Faith-77, Francop-76)
    m.s. "Nautila" Schiffahrtsges mbH & Co.
NAUTILA (ATG)   74   2075 2500   81.41   13.42   4.90 13.5 gen(144c)
    (ex Leana-95, Cranz-90, Aros Olympic-81, Ute Wulff-80, Galway-79, Ute Wulff-77, American Apache-77, launched as Ute Wulff)
    m.s. "Philipp" Schiffahrtsgesellschaft mbH & Co.
PHILIPP (ATG)   78   2567 2937   88.42   15.47   4.85 14.7 gen(208c)
    (ex SCL Clipper-98, Philipp-98, Karat-94, Rhein Lagan-94, Ile de France-93, Karat-82, Magnolia-78, launched as Karat)
    Partenreederei m.s. "Bell Swift"
SWIFT (ATG)   76   2973 3850   93.53   14.53   6.05 14.0 gen(205c)
    (ex Bell Swift-97, Jan-91, Arfell-90, Jan-87)

WOLFGANG GRIMPE SCHIFFAHRTS KG
Garbrecht & Grimpe Schiffahrts KG m.s. "Julia Isabel"
JULIA ISABEL (ATG) 92   2446 3735   87.90   12.80   5.50 10.6 gen(176c)
    (ex Saar Berlin-96, Julia Isabel-95)

DIETMAR GROTHMANN
Grothmann Schiffahrts-KG m.s. "Andrea"

ANDREA	(ATG)	81	1939	2890	87.97	11.33	4.67	11.5 gen(90c)

(ex Lania-98, Carola-94)

KAPITAN HEINZ HAACK
m.s. "Marjesco" Haack Schiffahrts KG

MARJESCO	(ATG)	88	2184	2735	82.02	12.70	4.71	11.5 gen(138c)

(ex Unitas H-96)

PAUL HÄSE KG

TUDOR	(DEU)	84	1296	1380	79.58	10.04	3.14	10.5 gen(72c)

(ex Kirsten-88)

WIDOR	(DEU)	87	1412	1780	80.96	11.38	3.29	10.5 gen

Paul Häse m.s. "Eldor" KG

ELDOR	(DEU)	81	1441	1795	80.96	11.33	3.29	10.5 gen(80c)

m.s. "Tirador" Eldor Häse KG

TIRADOR	(DEU)	97	1596	2220	88.95	11.40	3.70	10.5 gen

Having left Moerdijk earlier in the day, the **TUDOR** hurries down the New Waterway on her way to Rouen on 19 August 1999. (Peter Stewart)

HAMM SCHIFFAHRTS KG
Reinhard Hamm KG m.s. "Annegret"

ANNEGRET	(ATG)	95	3998	5218	101.10	18.45	6.50	15.5 gen(509c)

m.s. "Margret" Reinhard Hamm KG

MEDITERRANEO

	(ATG)	93	3992	5350	99.95	18.44	6.56	15.5 gen(516c)

(ex Margret-99)

HAMMANN & PRAHM REEDEREI GmbH & Co. KG

LORE PRAHM   (DEU) 89   1156   1323   58.00   11.80   3.56   9.5   gen(50c)
WALTER HAMMANN
      (DEU)   88   1156   1323   58.75   11.74   3.53   9.5   gen(50c)
      Hammann & Prahm Reedereiges mbH & Co. KG m.s. "Eric Hammann"
ERIC HAMMANN
      (DEU)   91   1156   1323   58.75   11.73   3.55   9.5   gen(50c)
      Reederei Hammann & Prahm GmbH & Co. KG m.s. "Evert Prahm"
EVERT PRAHM
      (DEU)   96   1598   2390   78.25   11.65   4.50   11.0   gen
      Hammann & Prahm Bereederungsges mbH & Co. KG m.s. "Gerhard Prahm"
GERHARD PRAHM
      (DEU)   82   1022   1089   74.50   9.50   2.88   10.0   gen
      (ex RMS Bavaria-96, Gerhard Prahm-92)
      Hammann & Prahm Bereederungsges mbH & Co. KG m.s. "Martha Hammann"
MARTHA HAMMANN
      (DEU)   85   1832   2287   80.68   12.70   4.17   11.0   gen(112c)
      Reederei Hammann & Prahm GmbH & Co. KG m.s. "Rebecca Hammann"
REBECCA HAMMANN
      (DEU)   95   1595   2420   76.40   11.65   4.48   10.7   gen
      Hammann & Prahm Reedereiges mbH & Co. m.s. "Selene Prahm"
SELENE PRAHM
      (DEU)   94   1594   2422   75.10   11.65   4.40   10.7   gen
      Hammann & Prahm Bereederungsges mbH & Co. KG m.s. "Sheila Hammann"
SHEILA HAMMANN
      (DEU)   83   1022   1113   74.50   9.53   2.88   10.0   gen
      (ex RMS Anglia-96, Sheila Hammann-92)

The **LORE PRAHM** passes Tilbury Landing Stage as she heads up the River Thames to Tilbury Dock on 30 September 2000.   (Kevin Bassett)

WOLFGANG HAMMANN KG

BAUMWALL	(DEU)	95	3999	5000	100.15	15.50	6.50	14.5	gen/pt(246c)

Reederei m.s. "Tista" Wolfgang Hammann KG

TISTA	(DEU)	78	2096	2240	83.80	12.83	4.40	12.0	gen(109c)

(ex Lys Vista-00, Tista-98)

Reederei m.s. "Tistedal" Wolfgang Hammann KG

TISTEDAL	(DEU)	96	4464	4600	116.00	16.60	5.05	15.2	gen(139c)

(ex Lyspol-99, Tistedal-98)

The **BAUMWALL** is a purpose-built pallet carrier and container ship. She is seen at Copenhagen on 29 October 1999. (the late Ove Nielsen)

HANSEATIC SCHIFFAHRT UND SCHIFFSMANAGEMENT GmbH

HANSEATIC SAILOR

	(ATG)	84	2191	1429	77.70	13.16	3.51	10.75	gen(120c)

(ex Bremer Reeder-01)

HÄNSEL SCHIFFAHRTS-UND BEREEDERUNGS GmbH & Co. KG

Hänsel Schiffahrts GmbH & Co m.s. "Katrin"

DUISBURG	(ATG)	86	1939	2859	89.03	12.51	4.33	10.0	gen(158c)

(ex Phini-99, Erika H.-97, Wilma-92)

Hänsel Schiffahrts GmbH & Co m.s. "Handorf"

HANDORF	(ATG)	86	1790	2800	82.50	12.60	4.52	11.5	gen(142c)

(ex Jacqueline-99, Jutta R-90, Jacqueline-86)

Hänsel Schiffahrts GmbH & Co m.s. "Henriette"

HENRIETTE	(ATG)	85	1949	2861	89.31	12.53	4.35	10.0	gen(158c)

(ex Katja-99, Dafi-99, Mete-99, Suzie-95, Six Madun-95)

Hänsel Schiffahrts GmbH & Co m.s. "Mark"

HOMBERG	(ATG)	85	1950	2871	85.53	12.53	4.36	10.0	gen(158c)

(ex Elisabeth-WE-99, Elisabeth W-86)

Hänsel Schiffahrts GmbH & Co m.s. "Ingrid"

JUPITER	(ATG)	85	1839	2167	78.59	12.70	4.25	12.0	gen(124c)

(ex Dirk-86)

Hänsel Schiffahrts GmbH & Co m.s. "Laura"

LAURA	(ATG)	82	1939	2890	87.97	11.33	4.67	11.5	gen(90c)

(ex Ilka-98)

Hänsel Schiffahrts GmbH & Co m.s. "Munster"

MÜNSTER	(ATG)	85	1948	3051	89.31	12.53	4.67	10.0	gen(158c)

(ex Jade-99, Sea Jade-88)

Hänsel Schiffahrts GmbH & Co m.s. "Nadine"

NADINE	(ATG)	79	2862	2507	98.70	15.96	3.76	12.5	gen(204c)

(ex Canopus I-00, Canopus-94)

Pennysmart Shipping Co. Ltd.

PAHNA	(CYP)	85	1951	2861	89.39	12.51	4.37	10.0	gen(158c)

(ex Nadine-97, Niels-92)

Hänsel Schiffahrts GmbH & Co m.s. "Vera"

VERA	(ATG)	80	2958	2811	98.81	15.96	4.07	13.5	gen(204c)

(ex Diogo Bernardes-00, Cassiopeia-86)

Hänsel Schiffahrts GmbH & Co m.s. "Munster" KG

WALSUM	(ATG)	77	1475	2271	69.02	13.54	4.50	9.0	gen

(ex Medway-99, Sea Medway-94)

HARMSTORF SHIPMANAGEMENT & ENGINEERING Co. Ltd.

Conway Castle Shipping Ltd.

MARIE-THERESE

(ATG)	90	3113	3487	92.70	15.12	5.31	12.0	gen(270c)

(ex Straits Joy-98, Wotan-96, Frank Konecny-95)

HARREN & PARTNER SCHIFFAHRTS GmbH

Ems-Fracht Schiffahrtsges mbH & Co. KG m.s. "Emstal"

EMSTAL	(ATG)	94	3791	4766	100.60	16.50	5.90	15.7	gen(390c)

(ex OPDR Douro-99, Emstal-95)

Harren & Partner Schiffahrts-GmbH & Co. KG m.s. "Palucca"

PALUCCA	(DEU)	97	4004	5270	104.75	16.57	6.57	16.0	gen(432c)

(ex Stadt Augsburg-00)

Harren & Partner Schiffahrts-GmbH m.s. "Paramar"

PARAMAR	(IOM)	98	2835	4128	89.72	13.60	5.70	13.5	gen(261c)

Harren & Partner Schiffahrtsges. mbH & Co. KG m.s. "Paranga"

RHEIN MASTER

(ATG)	94	3790	4766	100.60	16.50	5.90	15.0	gen(380c)

(ex Rhein Lagan-96, Paranga-95)

Ems-Fracht Schiffahrts GmbH & Co. KG m.s. "Rheintal"

RHEINTAL	(DEU)	96	3830	4766	93.00	16.50	5.89	16.3	gen(390c)

(ex Calderon-97, Rheintal-96)

Reederei Harren & Partner Schiffahrts-GmbH & Co. KG m.s. "Paragon"

SOLYMAR	(IOM)	98	2835	4128	89.72	13.60	5.70	13.5	gen(261c)

Harren & Partner Schiffahrts-GmbH & Co. KG m.s. "Pasadena"

SPIRIT OF RESOLUTION

(ANT)	97	3790	4766	100.60	16.50	5.90	15.0	gen(380c)

(ex Pasadena-98)

Harren & Partner Schiffahrts-GmbH & Co. m.s. "Paphos"

TRANSMAR	(GBR)	98	2820	4128	89.72	13.60	5.70	13.5	gen(261c)

(launched as Paphos)

Harren & Partner Schiffahrts-GmbH & Co. KG m.s. "Papagena"
ULTRAMAR (IOM) 97 2835 4128 89.72 13.60 5.70 13.5 gen(261c)
  (launched as Papagena)
Harren & Partner Schiffahrts-GmbH & Co. KG m.s. "Palmetto"
ZIM HONDURAS
  (ATG) 97 4004 5243 104.75 16.40 6.55 16.0 gen(432c)
  (ex Zim Venezuela IV-01, Stadt Essen-00)
Also larger ships.

HARTMANN SCHIFFAHRTS GmbH & CO. KG
Arrow Prince Shipping Co. Ltd.
FLEVO (CYP) 91 2497 4195 88.29 13.21 5.40 11.0 gen
  (ex Waltraud-92, Kirsten-91)
Bell Raider Shipping Co. Ltd.
GARMO (CYP) 94 2901 4228 91.20 13.80 5.80 12.5 gen(241c)
  (launched as Ilka)
Coral Master Shipping Co. Ltd.
HAUGO (CYP) 94 2811 4206 91.20 13.85 5.80 12.5 gen(190c)
  (launched as Niels)
Ray International Ltd.
JANE (LBR) 86 3230 3937 100.49 14.15 5.27 12.0 gen(240c)
  (ex Jan Luiken-98, Deepsea Carrier-89, launched as Jan Luiken Eltes)
Florino Shipping Co. Ltd.
LAURA HELENA
  (CYP) 93 2811 4206 91.20 13.80 5.75 12.5 gen(190c)
Also larger ships.

BEREEDERUNGSBÜRO KAPITÄN LAURENZ HELD
Ems-Trans Schiffahrtsges. mbH & Co. KG m.s. "Isartal"
ISARTAL (ATG) 89 2369 2760 87.90 12.90 5.49 11.8 gen(144c)
m.s. "Marie Chris" Schiffahrts-GmbH & Co. KG
LYS-CHRIS (ATG) 93 2416 3750 84.95 13.03 4.48 12.0 gen(197c)
  (ex Marie Chris-93)

HELMSING & GRIMM (GmbH & CO.)
Cancyp Maritime Ltd.
ELISABETH (CYP) 69 2851 4179 96.14 14.66 5.91 14.0 gen
  (Eskdalegate-77, Fredericksgate-74, Bruni-74)
Fione Panama Inc.
FIONE (PAN) 67 2451 3770 96.17 13.52 5.90 13.0 gen
  (Abdul Razaak Sanusi-79, Gratia-77)
Eurafrican Shipping Ltd.
JOHN C. HELMSING
  (CYP) 67 2451 3780 98.14 13.54 5.91 13.5 gen
  (ex Fiducia-75)
Mariann Panama Inc.
MARIANN (PAN) 75 1953 3015 91.37 13.31 5.12 14.0 gen
Eurotramp Navigation Co. Ltd.
THERESE (CYP) 72 1953 3015 91.37 13.31 5.12 14.0 gen
Also larger ships.

REEDEREI KLAUS HESSE

Accent Shipping Co. Ltd.
JAMBO (CYP) 90 1990 3677 88.15 14.18 5.00 10.5 gen
Black Whale Shipping Co. Ltd.
PLATO (CYP) 89 1990 3677 88.15 14.18 5.27 12.0 gen

ALFRED HINSCH KG

m.s. "Unitas-H" Hinsch Schiffahrtsges. mbH & Co. KG
UNITAS-H (DEU) 97 2835 4140 90.50 13.60 5.73 13.0 gen(372c)
(ex Geestborg-01, Unitas-H-97)
m.s. "Veritas-H" Hinsch Schiffahrtsges. mbH & Co. KG
VERITAS-H (ATG) 95 2899 3950 97.83 16.44 4.90 15.0 cc(340c)
(ex Regulus-97, Veritas-H-96)

When photographed heading eastwards along the Kiel Canal on 15 September 1999, the **VERITAS-H** was working for Team Lines on her regular route linking Gdynia to Hamburg and Bremerhaven. (Barry Standerline)

HENRY HORSTMANN

m.s. "Lennard" Schiffahrts-KG
LENNARD (DEU) 01 1550 2150 gen

HERMANN HORWEGE

KAJA-H (ATG) 69 1251 1408 74.12 10.90 3.66 10.0 gen
(ex Castor-98)

GEBR. HULLMANN

HERMANN G (DEU) 28 146 288 38.00 5.57 1.91 9.0 gen
(ex Bernd-Birgit-74, Fridmariwalt-68)

JOHANNES ICK
Partenreederei m.s. "Detlef Schmidt"
MARIANNE (DEU) 78 1934 2415 79.23 13.54 3.99 12.5 gen(142c)
(ex Detlef Schmidt-94)

WEERT IHNEN & CO.
NORDERTOR (DEU) 60 156 247 42.47 5.82 1.98 8.5 tk
(ex Nordbunker XI-82, Nordbunker XII, Weser)

INTERORIENT NAVIGATION HAMBURG GmbH
m.s. "Arneb" Schiffahrtsges. mbH & Co. KG
ARNEB (DEU) 86 3640 1523 88.73 14.30 5.11 13.0 gen/ro(214c)
(ex Alster Rapid-95)
Also larger ships.

INTERSCAN SCHIFFAHRTSGESELLSCHAFT mbH
Schiffahrtsgesellschaft m.s. "Pamela" Interscan Reederei GmbH & Co.
PAMELA (DEU) 85 1586 1738 83.38 11.31 3.52 10.5 gen(48c)
(ex Boberg-88)
m.s. "Patria" Interscan Reederei GmbH & Co.
PATRIA (GIB) 95 2210 3519 82.38 12.56 5.71 13..0 gen(154c)
m.s. "Patriot" Interscan Shipping GmbH & Co.
PATRIOT (CYP) 94 2163 3086 82.44 12.56 5.24 12.0 gen(106c)
Provence Navigation Ltd.
PEIKKO (CYP) 83 1521 1723 82.48 11.38 3.55 10.7 gen(80c)
(ex Sabine L-98, RMS Germania-95, Sabine L-92)
m.s. "Phantom" Interscan Bereederungs GmbH & Co. KG
PHANTOM (GIB) 00 2150 3275 82.45 12.50 5.45 12.5 gen(156c)
m.s. "Pinta" Interscan Shipping GmbH & Co.
PINTA (DEU) 93 2190 2795 82.30 12.56 4.91 11.0 gen(88c)
Pionier Wolter Schiffahrtsgesellschaft mbH & Co.
PIONIER (CYP) 89 2270 2801 82.30 12.50 4.88 11.0 gen(137c)
m.s. "Premiere" Interscan Reederei GmbH & Co.
PREMIERE (DEU) 85 1649 1631 82.45 11.33 3.43 10.5 gen(46c)
m.s. "Sooneck" Interscan Schiffsbetriebsges mbH & Co. KG
SOONECK (ATG) 86 1616 2019 82.48 11.31 3.90 10.0 gen(108c)
Newbuilding:
PROTEUS (DEU) 01 2150 3275 82.50 12.50 5.50 gen(155c)
Also larger ships.

INTERSEE SCHIFFAHRTS-GESELLSCHAFT mbH
m.s. "Claudia" Schiffahrtsges. mbH & Co. Reederei KG
CLAUDIA (ANT) 00 2218 3400 89.40 12.50 5.15 12.0 gen(154c)
m.s. "Lydia" Schiffahrtsges. mbH & Co. Reederei KG
LYDIA (ANT) 00 2218 3650 89.40 12.50 5.22 11.5 gen(154c)
m.s. "Michelle" Schiffahrtsges. mbH & Co. Reederei KG
MICHELLE (ATG) 00 2996 5050 95.16 13.17 6.06 12.2 gen(213c)
m.s. "Nicola" Schiffahrtsges. mbH & Co. Reederei KG
NICOLA (NLD) 00 2990 5050 95.16 13.17 6.06 12.2 gen(213c)
m.s. "Wannsee" Schiffahrtsges. mbH & Co. Reederei KG
NORDSTRAND
(ATG) 91 2440 3232 87.48 13.01 5.08 12.0 gen(202c)
(ex MF Malta-01, Intermodal Egypt-96, Wannsee-94, Medeur Terzo-92, Wannsee-92)

m.s. "Petra" Schiffahrtsges. mbH & Co. Reederei KG									
PETRA	(ANT)	01	2545	3850	88.60	12.50	5.40	13.0	gen
m.s. "Sandra" Schiffahrtsges. mbH & Co. Reederei KG									
SANDRA	(ANT)	01	2000	3400	88.60	12.50	5.49	13.0	gen
m.s. "Vera" Schiffahrtsges. mbH & Co. Reederei KG									
VERA	(ANT)	00	2218	3400	89.40	12.50	5.21	12.0	gen(154c)

GERHARD JACOBS

HAMMELWARDEN

(DEU)	60	388	608	55.25	7.27	2.56	9.0	gen

HEINZ-GEORG JACOBS

RIA	(DEU)	60	337	443	46.49	8.49	2.69	9.0	gen

(ex Thea K-89, Castor-70, Moni-65)

ERICH JAGEMANN

STELLA MARIS

(DEU)	67	824	788	61.98	9.86	3.29	10.0	gen

GUNTER JANSSEN

OLAF J.	(PAN)	37	284	520	39.14	7.04	3.07	8.0	gen

(ex Dirk Rust-79, Hans-Georg-64)

JENS & WALLER KG

m.s. "Helene" Jens u. Waller KG									
NYLAND	(DEU)	95	2996	4622	99.95	16.74	5.95	15.0	gen(326c)
m.s. "Wilhelm" Jens & Waller KG									
VÄRMLAND	(DEU)	95	2997	4624	99.95	16.74	5.95	15.0	gen(326c)

(launched as Wilhelm)

Another container feeder ship also working for Team Lines and also on the Kiel Canal, the **VÄRMLAND** heads for Hamburg from the Baltic on 14 July 1999. (Dominic McCall)

REEDEREI LUTZ JESKE
Partenreederei MS "Traveberg"
TRAVEBERG (CYP) 75 2287 2580 81.41 13.42 5.03 13.75 gen(149c)
(ex Patria-94, American Comanche-78)
Partenreederei MS "Weserberg"
WESERBERG (PMD) 76 2239 2560 81.36 13.44 5.03 13.75 gen(150c)
(ex Pico Grande-00, Gotland-87, Jacob Becker-86)

UWE JESS REEDEREI
Partenreederei m.s. "Nordwind"
NORDWIND (CYP) 76 2161 1800 86.80 12.83 4.74 13.0 gen(115c)
Walter Jess Schiffahrtsgesellschaft KG
NORDSEE (ATG) 78 2579 2954 88.68 15.47 4.85 14.7 gen(208c)
(ex Seaboard Clipper-99, Nordsee-96)

JUHLKE SCHIFFAHRTS GmbH
ELBE STAR (CYP) 84 3777 4596 97.08 17.20 5.22 12.0 gen(259c)
(ex Pul Sejathera-92, Rex Star-90)

KLAUS JULS
KORMORAN (ATG) 65 658 743 55.07 9.23 3.26 10.0 gen
(ex Dorte Star-89, Milla Star-84, Dorte Star-81, Harle Riff-72)

HEINZ-ALFRED JUNGKLAUS
GRAUERORT (DEU) 65 449 684 56.72 7.17 2.76 9.0 gen

JÜNGERHANS & CO. REEDEREIVERWALTUNG
Astor Schiffahrts GmbH & Co. KG m.s. "Adele J"
ADELE J. (ATG) 91 2481 3269 87.42 13.00 5.08 12.0 gen(153c)
(ex MF Mare-99, Intermodal Mare-96, Trident Star-95, Adele J-93, Medeur Secondo-93, Adele J-93)
Sirius Schiffahrts GmbH & Co. KG m.s. "Adele J"
ANGELA J (ATG) 95 3804 4766 99.80 16.50 5.80 14.5 gen(390c)
(ex CMBT Cruiser-96, launched as Angela J)
Astor Schiffahrts GmbH & Co. KG m.s. "Anna J"
ANNA J. (ATG) 93 2480 3269 87.42 13.00 5.08 12.0 gen(153c)
(ex MF Egypt-99, Intermodal Egypt-96, Anna J-93)
Sirius Schiffahrts GmbH & Co. KG m.s. "Carina J"
CARINA J. (ATG) 90 2463 3200 87.42 13.00 5.08 12.0 gen(153c)
(ex Coastal Breeze-00, Hanni J-98, Herm J-98, Cari-Star-94, Primo-92, Medeur Primo-92, Rhein Carrier-91, Herm J-90)
Sirius Schiffahrts GmbH & Co. KG m.s. "Ingo J"
INGO J. (ATG) 91 2480 3237 87.37 13.02 4.70 12.0 gen(153c)
(ex MF Levant-99, Intermodal Levant-96, Diana J-93, Queensee-93)
Astor Schiffahrts GmbH & Co. KG m.s. "Stephan J"
MEKONG PIONEER
(ATG) 95 3833 4766 100.60 16.50 5.90 15.0 gen(390c)
(ex Stephan J-00)
Astor Schiffahrts GmbH & Co. KG m.s. "Gerd J"
P & O NEDLLOYD OBOCK
(DEU) 97 3850 4766 100.60 16.50 5.90 15.0 gen(384c)
(ex Gerd J-00, Cagema St. Lucia-99, Gerd J-97)

Astor Schiffahrts GmbH & Co. KG m.s. "Doris J"
P & O NEDLLOYD TRINIDAD
    (DEU)   97   3850 4750   100.60 16.50   5.90 15.0 gen(384c)
    (ex Doris J-00)
Sirius Schiffahrts GmbH & Co. KG m.s. "Regina J"
REGINA J (ATG)   94   3806 4766   100.63 16.50   5.91 15.0 gen(390c)
    (ex Bremer Handel-99, Regina J-97)
Astor Schiffahrts GmbH & Co. KG m.s. "Sagitta J"
SAGITTA J. (ATG)   91   2481 3237   87.42 13.00   5.08 12.5 gen(202c)
    (ex Coastal Bay-01, Rhein Feeder-96, Rhein Lee-94, Rhein Feeder-93, Liesel I-91)
Sirius Schiffahrts GmbH & Co. KG m.s. "Anke J"
SEABOARD SPIRIT
    (ATG)   85   2295 2596   95.92 14.10   4.07 10.0 gen/ro(180c)
    (ex Anke J-97, Anke S-96, Dyggve-94, RMS Alemannia-94, Anke S-92)
Astor Schiffahrts GmbH & Co. KG m.s. "Simone J"
SIMONE J (DEU)   97   3840 4635   100.60 16.50   5.90 15.0 gen(384c)
Kaduto Schiffahrts GmbH & Co. KG m.s. "Tim"
TIM (DEU)   97   3850 4766   100.60 16.50   5.90 15.0 gen(384c)
    (ex Cagema St. Vincent-99, Tim-97)
Kaduto Schiffahrts GmbH & Co. KG m.s. "Bernd"
VANGUARD (ATG)   94   3806 4766   100.63 16.50   5.91 15.0 gen(390c)
    (ex Cari Sea-95, Angela J-94)
Astor Schiffahrts GmbH & Co. KG m.s. "Heide J"
ZIM EASTMED (ATG) 92   2481 3221   87.42 13.00   5.08 12.0 gen(153c)
    (ex MF Carrier-99, Intermodal Carrier-96, Rhein Carrier-95, Heide J-93)
Also larger ships.

CHRISTIAN JÜRGENSEN + BRINK & WÖLFFEL

m.s. "Barbara" Reederei H.G. Sassmannshausen KG
BARBARA (DEU)   96   2984 4850   98.43 16.50   5.91 15.5 cc(332c)
m.s. "Bonnie Rois" Reederei H.-M. Ludtke KG
BONNIE ROIS (DEU) 98   2986 4830   98.43 16.90   5.91 14.5 cc(366c)
Partenreederei m.s. "Johanna"
COASTAL ISLE
    (DEU)   91   3125 2973   89.10 16.18   4.85 14.6 gen(258c)
    (ex Johanna-97)
Reederei Jürgen Speck KG
EIDER (DEU)   78   1934 2495   91.79 13.54   3.99 12.5 gen
KG Bulkmaster Shipping GmbH & Co.
EVA MARIA MÜLLER
    (DEU)   98   2450 3680   87.90 12.80   5.49 11.7 gen(164c)
Jan Peter Ludtke KG
INGA (DEU)   85   1584 1783   82.02 11.49   3.51 15.5 gen
m.s. "Jenna Catherine" Reederei H.M. Ludtke KG
JENNA CATHERINE
    (DEU)   95   2966 4830   98.43 16.90   5.93 15.0 gen(366c)
Hans-Michael Ludtke KG
LEONA (DEU)   87   1593 1900   82.02 11.49   3.67 10.0 gen
    (ex Scot Carrier-94, launched as Leona)
KG Bulktrader Shipping GmbH & Co.
MONIKA MÜLLER
    (DEU)   98   2450 3680   87.90 12.80   5.49 11.7 gen(164c)

Walter Meyer Schiffahrts KG m.s. "Priwall"

PRIWALL (CYP) 92 2446 3735 87.90 12.80 5.50 10.5 gen(176c)

m.s. "Sybille" Reederei Ludtke KG

SYBILLE (DEU) 91 3125 4485 89.11 16.18 6.14 14.6 gen(260c)
(ex Rhein Merchant-00, Sybille-95, Baltic Bridge-93, Sybille-93)

m.s. "Ute Johanna" Reederei Hans-Erich und Jan-Peter Ludtke KG

UTE JOHANNA (DEU) 95 2984 4850 98.43 17.09 5.86 15.0 cc(366c)

Reederei m.s. "Wotan " Walter Meyer Schiffahrts-KG

WOTAN (DEU) 96 2997 4450 99.75 12.80 5.63 13.5 gen(300c)

JOHANN KAHRS KG

m.s. "Uwe Kahrs" GmbH & Co. KG

UWE KAHRS (DEU) 97 3995 5865 99.95 18.20 6.61 17.0 cc(523c)
(ex Maersk Messina-99, Uwe Kahrs-98)

Also the larger THEA KAHRS.

"KEVIN S" GmbH & Co. KG

KEVIN S (ATG) 68 872 1400 59.70 10.04 4.50 11.0 gen(30c)
(ex Hemo-00, Antje B-96, Claus-86)

KIEPE-SCHEPERS K.G. SCHIFFAHRT

Schepers-Rheintrader Schiffahrts KG

RHEIN TRADER
(DEU) 91 3815 4155 103.50 16.24 6.07 14.5 gen(372c)
(ex Rhein Lee-93, Rhein Trader-93)

Also larger ships.

HUBERTUS KLOSE

IRIS-JÖRG (DEU) 56 281 433 45.34 8.03 2.57 9.0 gen
(ex Seestern-65, Eilenburg-64)

The **LASBEK** was photographed off Santander on 17 June 1995.   (Barry Standerline)

KNOHR & BURCHARD NFL. (GmbH & Co.)

Frigatebird Shipping Co. N.V.
ISEBEK (LBR)   96   3711 5700   99.90   16.48   6.72 15.0 oil/ch tk
(ex Multitank Saxonia-97)
Andrena Shipping Co. Ltd.
JERSBEK (LBR)   82   2690 3872   91.72   13.72   6.23 12.5 ch tk
(ex Cape Island-87)
Bendrena Shipping Co. Ltd.
LASBEK (LBR)   84   2699 4028   91.72   13.62   6.43 12.5 ch tk
(ex Sandy Island-87)

HERMANN UND GERDA KOPPLEMANN

Partenreederei KR Gebr. Koppelmann
ALTELAND (DEU)   95   2996 4602   99.95   16.74   5.96 15.5 gen(326c)
(launched as Patria)

JÖRG KÖPPING SHIPPING CO.

Partenreederei m.s. "Rendsburg"
ARGANA (MAR)   91   3469 4706   95.65   15.82   6.02 14.0 gen(343c)
(ex Rendsburg-99, Ruth Borchard-97, Rendsburg-91)
Jorg Kopping Verwaltungsgesellschaft mbH & Co. m.s. "Marburg" KG
GEEST MERCHANT
(ATG)   95   2899 3916   99.27   16.20   4.90 16.0 cc(340c)
(ex Marburg-97)
Jorg Kopping Schiffahrtsgesellsxhaft mbH & Co. m.s. "Limburg" KG
GEEST TRADER
(ATG)   95   2899 3950   99.21   16.44   4.91 14.5 cc(340c)
(ex Limburg-95)
Partenreederei Jorg Kopping m.s. "Hamburg"
HAMBURG (ATG)   91   3466 4707   99.65   15.82   6.01 14.0 gen(343c)
(ex Judith Borchard-97, Hamburg-91)

GERHARD KRAWINKEL

GERHARD K (DEU)   67   418   645   54.97   7.17   2.91   9.0 gen

KARL-HEINZ KRUSE

TINA (DEU)   60   328   518   47.15   7.27   2.56   8.0 gen
(ex Timo-94, Freiheit-78)

REEDEREI UWE KRUSE

Partenreederei m.s. "Svealand"
DUNKERQUE EXPRESS II
(DEU)   75   2240 2380   81.49   13.44   5.03 10.0 gen(149c)
(ex Ulla-89, Osteclipper-86, Nic Clipper-79, Osteclipper-78)
Partenreederei m.s. "Lappland"
LA ROCHELLE EXPRESS
(DEU)   75   2240 2560   81.39   13.42   5.03 13.7 gen(149c)
(ex Lappland-97, Yankee Clipper-93, Lappland-79, Manchester Falcon-76, launched as
Lappland)
Also tugs.

The River Ouse presents a calm appearance as the **CHARLOTTE** passes Whitgift on her way upriver on New Year's Day 2000. (John S Mattison)

The **MULTITANK IBERIA** was photographed on 28 May 2001 in the River Mersey as she approached Eastham at the end of a voyage from Bayonne. (David Williams)

The **IDA RAMBOW** sails sedately along the Swale as she approaches Ridham Dock in Kent on 28 September 1999. (Kevin Bassett)

Although owned by a German company, the **SELENE PRAHM** and her fleetmates are managed by Leafe and Hawkes, based in Hull. She was photographed at Southampton on 7 June 1997. (Brian Ralfs)

Seen heading up Southampton Water from Dublin on 8 June 2000, the **GERD SIBUM** sailed later the same day to Antwerp.   (Chris Bancroft)

The **ALADIN** is an example of a standard class of low air draught coaster built at the Hugo Peters yard in Wewelsfleth. She was photographed as she arrived at Cardiff on 4 November 2000 to load scrap for El Ferrol in Spain.   (Nigel Jones)

The **ILKA** is seen arriving in the Lincolnshire port of Boston at the end of a voyage from the Baltic on the sunny morning of 20 July 2000. This coaster has strong links with Husum, being built, registered and owned in this German port. (Richard Potter)

The **ROLF BUCK** leaves Goole on 29 December 1999 at the start of one of her regular voyages to Rotterdam. (Roy Cressey)

JÖRG KULL

ELVI KULL (ATG)   55   474   730   57.92   8.06   2.93   8.5   gen
(ex Jens Peter-84, Reinhold Krusemark-62)

L & L SHIPPING

Quickco Shipping Ltd.

LUCKY (CYP)   82   1934   2890   87.97   11.54   4.70   11.0   gen(90c)
(ex Poetenitz-99, Diogo do Cuoto-95, Svenja-86)

Partenreederei m.s. "Dixi"

NANDIA (CYP)   82   1939   2886   87.97   11.30   4.66   11.5   gen(90c)
(ex Birte Wehr-99, Humber Star-99, Birte Wehr-95, Katja-90)

Seen loading china clay at Par on 21 April 2000, the **NANDIA** is a regular visitor to Cornwall's
clay ports.   (Dominic McCall)

REEDEREI F. LAEISZ GmbH

COASTAL WAVE
(DEU)   83   2046   1874   77.96   13.85   5.02   13.0   gen(124c)
(ex Pellworm-98, Neptunus-95, Craigantlet-88)

Also larger ships.

REEDEREI LEHMANN

m.s. "Alessandra Lehmann" Schiffahrt KG

AGILA (ATG)   95   2997   4550   97.27   16.15   5.93   14.8   gen(304c)
(launched as Alessandra Lehmann)

Hans Lehmann KG

ANNA LEHMANN
(ATG)   00   2820   4111   90.00   13.60   5.71   12.0   gen(261c)
HANS LEHMANN
(MMR)   78   2359   3182   94.80   12.83   4.66   12.0   gen(185c)
HEIKE LEHMANN
(ATG)   85   2564   3050   87.91   12.81   4.50   11.0   gen(153c)

KARIN LEHMANN								
(ATG)	00	2835	4111	90.00	13.60	5.71	13.0	gen(261c)
LISA LEHMANN								
(DEU)	89	2643	3180	87.99	13.03	4.87	11.0	gen(153c)
MARIE LEHMANN								
(DEU)	87	2642	3017	87.99	13.03	4.38	11.0	gen(198c)
SIEGFRIED LEHMANN								
(MMR)	80	2225	2570	80.80	13.44	5.04	13.0	gen(154c)

Launched as **ALESSANDRA LEHMANN**, the **AGILA** is on charter to Pal Line and is seen here approaching Goole from Oskarshamn on 27 August 2000. (Richard Potter)

HEINZ LITMEYER SCHIFFAHRTS KG
Heli Schiffahrts Verwaltungs GmbH & Co. KG m.s. "Emsland"

EMSLAND (ATG)	84	1857	2200	80.17	12.65	4.18	10.5	gen(102c)

LÖWER SCHIFFAHRTSGESELLSCHAFT mbH
Partenreederei m.s. "Rangitoto"

NOUMEA EXPRESS

(ATG)	84	3120	3654	88.63	15.70	6.44	13.8	gen(256c)

(ex Rangitoto-97, Blue Wave-92, Sleipner-91, Brynmore-88, Sleipner-87)

Partenreederei m.s. "Rangitane"

RANGITANE (ATG)	84	3120	4134	88.52	15.70	6.45	13.8	gen(256c)

(ex Antje B-93, Osprey-88, Antje-87, Band Aid Carrier-86, Antje-85)

HERMANN LOHMANN SCHIFFAHRTSVERWALTUNGS GmbH
Hermann Lohmann Schiffahrtsgesellschaft mbH & Co. KG m.s. "Helen"

HELEN (ATG)	92	2446	3735	87.90	12.80	5.50	10.6	gen(184c)

(ex Pandora-99)

Hermann Lohmann Schiffahrtsgesellschaft mbH & Co. KG m.s. "NIKLAS"

NIKLAS (ATG)	92	2446	3735	87.90	12.80	4.45	10.6	gen(176c)

(ex Padua-99)

Hermann Lohmann Schiffahrts KG m.s. "Santa Maria"
SANTA MARIA (DEU) 85   3062 3670   99.42 14.03   5.10 12.0 gen(198c)

REEDEREI HELMUT LÜHRS
m.s. "Beate" Helmut Lührs KG
BEATE (DEU)   69   1223 1998   74.02 10.83   5.06 12.5 gen(63c)
(ex Stefanie-94, Cosmea-80, Elke Kahrs-84, Baltic Concord-74, launched as Elke Kahrs)
Reederei Helmut Lührs KG m.s. "Nina"
NINA (ATG)   79   1713 1640   79.51 12.83   3.46 12.25 gen(88c)
(ex Eberstein-99)
Syrena Shipping Ltd
SYRENA (ATG)   72   1777 2999   79.99 13.80   5.33 13.0 gen
(ex Maik Primo-95, Rudolf Kurz-81)

MARITIME - GESELLSCHAFT FÜR MARITIME DIENSTLEISTUNGEN mbH
Hazards Marine Inc.
JO CURACAO (LBR) 96   3335 4994   97.00 16.00   7.80 12.5 oil/ch tk
(ex Curaco-01, Capella-96)
Granger Maritime Co.
MULTITANK BATAVIA
        (LBR)   98   3726 5846   99.90 16.50   6.80 15.0 ch tk
Chemtrans Marine Ltd.
MULTITANK IBERIA
        (DEU)   95   3716 5797   99.99 16.50   6.72 15.0 ch tk
Also larger ships.

MATHIES SCHIFFAHRTS GmbH
Partenreederei m.s. "Gotaland"
GÖTALAND (DEU)   78   2578 2937   88.68 15.47   4.85 14.7 gen(208c)
(ex Helene Waller-94, Rachel Borchard-87, Helene Waller-86, Thiassi-79, Helene Waller-78)
Also the larger INGRID.

MEERPAHL & MEYER BEREEDERUNG
Partenreederei m.s. "Buxtehude"
BUXTEHUDE (CYP) 85   2565 3020   89.11 13.03   4.61 11.0 gen(153c)
(ex Rita-95)
Partenreederei m.s. "Wahlstedt"
HAMPOEL (CYP)   85   2568 3070   87.97 12.83   4.29 10.5 gen(153c)
(ex Wahlstedt-99, Monika Ehler-96)
Partenreederei m.s. "Leeswig"
LEESWIG (CYP)   85   2561 3065   87.94 12.86   4.60 11.0 gen(153c)
(ex Claus Jürgens-93)
Partenreederei m.s. "Radesforde"
RADESFORDE
        (ATG)   90   2606 3647   89.99 13.00   5.24 11.0 gen(198c)
(ex Johanna-98)
Partenreederei m.s. "Sierksdorf"
SIERKSDORF (ATG) 83   1963 2827   87.97 11.54   4.68 11.5 gen(86c)
(ex Montania-96, Meike-92, Faun-89, Frauke-86)

GÜNTER MEYER
Moana Shipping Co Ltd

UNIKA	(ATG)	71	1773	1426	76.56	12.83	4.06	12.2	gen(163c)

(ex Arnis-85)

HERBERT MEYER
Partenreederei m.s. "Karin"

KARIN	(DEU)	88	1986	2627	82.50	12.50	4.60	11.1	gen(98c)

SCHIFFAHRTSGESELLSCHAFT PETER MEYER KG

AROSIA	(ATG)	77	1678	2800	71.99	12.83	5.45	12.5	gen(128c)

(ex Corvette-90, Eco Dao-83, Corvette-81, Else Beth-78)

FLORA	(ATG)	78	3081	3798	93.27	14.53	6.76	14.0	gen(250c)

(ex Cellus-98, Hildegard Wulff-83)

BERND MEYERING SCHIFFAHRTS KG

AURA	(CYP)	92	2416	3570	84.95	13.03	5.44	12.0	gen(197c)

(ex Lyme Bay-97, Jens-93)

HEINZ MOJE
Schiffahrtsgesellschaft m.s. "Deneb" Heinz Moje KG

DENEB	(DEU)	94	3992	5350	101.13	18.44	6.55	15.5	gen(509c)

(ex OOCL Neva-98, Deneb-98, Rhein Partner-98, Rhein Liffey-95, launched as Deneb)

m.s. "Maris" Heinz Moje KG

MARIS	(DEU)	95	3996	5325	100.00	18.45	6.56	15.5	gen(508c)

HORST MÖLLER KG
Ariadna Shipping Ltd.

MANYA	(VCT)	67	1069	1205	68.43	10.52	3.92	10.5	gen

(ex Norasia Attika-93, Carsten-93)

Arne Thielen KG m.s. "Rika"

RIKA	(ATG)	78	1925	2271	79.79	12.83	4.43	12.0	gen(145c)

(ex Hanni-98, G. H. Ehler-90)

EWALD MÜLLER & Co. GmbH
Scheepvaartbedrijf De Haan

ALISSA	(NLD)	96	1143	1490	81.40	9.50	3.10	8.0	gen(50c)

m.s. "Ewald" Schiffahrts KG

EWALD	(DEU)	99	1599	2262	88.00	11.30	3.65	10.0	gen

Kaptain J. A. L. M. Wildenbeest

GEMINUS	(NLD)	71	402	564	55.00	7.22	2.16	10.0	gen

(ex Zuiderzee-85, Bornrif-83, Veritas-79, Dolfijn-75)

Rambler Shipping CV

RAMBLER	(NLD)	84	1171	1586	79.08	9.95	3.36	11.0	gen(72c)

(ex Jens-00, Scorpio-96, Morgenstond-92)

Hardinxveld Boat Charters B.V.

RIO-Y-MAR	(NLD)	73	505	721	60.41	7.90	2.79	9.0	gen

Kaptain Jan de Jonge

SCOUT MARIN	(NLD)	83	1035	1063	74.55	9.50	2.88	10.5	gen(66c)

(ex Wilke-93, Sea Dart-89, Wilke-88)

W. L. Mastenbroek

TIME IS MONEY

	(NLD)	73	804	1130	76.41	8.13	3.02	10.0	gen

(ex Meander-00, Latona-95)

N.C. SCHIFFAHRTSBÜRO GmbH & Co. KG

BALTICA (HND) 71 2397 2445 88.50 13.85 5.26 14.0 gen(128c)
(ex San Pancracio I-94, Baltica-85, Scol Hunter-77, Baltica-76)
Unisand Shipping Co. Ltd.
NORDICA (CYP) 80 3731 6275 80.70 15.85 8.32 12.5 gen(190c)
(ex Sandy Cay-99, Trinity Square-98, Louise Green-96, Oostzee-94, Savonia-83, Oostzee-81)

REEDEREI NAGEL KG

Jan Nagel Schiffahrts KG
GRIMM (DEU) 92 3564 4050 104.75 15.40 4.15 12.5 gen(154c)
m.s. "Kajen" Elbnautik Schiffahrts GmbH & Co. KG
KAJEN (DEU) 89 3555 3027 103.66 15.21 4.15 12.5 gen(157c)
(launched as Edina)
Also larger RACHEL BORCHARD.

NAUTIRA SCHIFFAHRTS GmbH

Ideal Shipping Co. Ltd.
ATLANTIC MERCADO
(ATG) 76 3422 3666 80.27 16.13 5.97 12.7 gen(165c)
(ex Eliza-90, Rijpgracht-89)

REEDEREI NIMMRICH & PRAHM GmbH & Co. KG

Nimmrich & Prahm Reederei GmbH & Co. KG m.s. "Christa
CHRISTA (CYP) 83 2795 2852 95.61 13.64 4.32 13.5 gen(157c)
m.s. "Odin" Reederei GmbH & Co. Schiffahrts KG
STADT PAPENBURG
(DEU) 81 2723 2860 95.91 13.52 4.29 12.5 gen(157c)
(ex Odin-97, Vela-91)

Having arrived at Copenhagen from Grangemouth on 28 November 1999, the **CHRISTA** was photographed as she departed on the following day. (the late Ove Nielsen)

NORDENHAMER BEREEDERUNGS-GESELLSCHAFT mbH

m.s. "Anja II" Schiffahrtsges. mbH & Co.
ANJA II (ATG) 91 2705 3982 89.48 13.50 5.34 12.0 gen(220c)
Partenreederei m.s. "Elke"
ELKE (ATG) 86 1473 2111 79.02 10.91 3.99 10.0 gen(80c)
Einswarden Shipping Co. Ltd.
EMMA (ATG) 85 3412 4104 95.97 16.24 6.35 14.0 gen(323c)
(ex Einswarden-98, Rangitata-98, Christa Thielemann-92, Nedlloyd Shuttle-91,
Christa Thielemann-89)
Partenreederei m.s. "Felix"
FELIX (ATG) 80 2610 4510 86.52 14.36 6.76 13.2 gen(140c)
(ex Leveche-94, Pacifico-94, Eve Pacific-93, Svea Pacific-93, Burro-88, Burro Bulk-86,
Astillero-86, Cabados-85, Duro Ocho-82)
Partenreederei m.s. "Gudrun II"
GUDRUN II (DEU) 87 1599 2262 80.31 11.31 4.37 11.0 gen(84c)
(ex Gudrun-90)
Partenreederei m.s. "Helga"
HELGA (ATG) 84 1472 2131 79.02 10.93 3.97 10.0 gen
(ex Fast Karel-98, Helga-94, Hanne-90)
Partenreederei m.s. "Hella"
HELLA (ATG) 85 1473 2086 79.02 10.93 3.97 10.0 gen(80c)
(ex Hel-92)
m.s. "Karin" Schiffahrtsges mbH & Co. KG
HMS PORTUGAL
(ATG) 96 3821 4698 100.63 16.50 5.90 15.0 gen(390c)
(ex Karin-96)
Partenreederei m.s. "Kirsten"
KIRSTEN (ATG) 85 1473 2127 79.02 10.91 3.97 12.0 gen(80c)
(ex Fast Wal-98, Kirsten-93, Sabine-93)
m.s. "Tettens" Schiffahrtsgesellschaft mbH & Co. KG
MONTE VERDE
(CPV) 97 4128 5184 100.62 16.20 6.40 15.5 gen(374c)
(ex MSC Frisia-99, Tettens-98)
m.s. "Volkers" Schiffahrtsges mbH & Co. KG
NENUFAR EUROPE
(ATG) 98 4155 4656 100.62 16.20 6.40 15.5 gen(380c)
(ex Volkers-01, MSC Vigo-01, Volkers-98)
m.s. "Blexen" Schiffahrt GmbH & Co. KG
PORTLINK CARAVEL
(ATG) 96 3821 4695 100.63 16.50 5.90 15.0 gen(390c)
(ex CMBT Caravel-98, Blexen-96, Heike-96)
m.v. "Sarah" Shipping Co. Ltd.
SARAH (ATG) 91 2705 3892 89.50 13.60 5.34 12.0 gen(218c)
(ex MSC Larisa-98, Sarah-97, Cortes-96, Sarah-96)
m.v. Scotia Shipping Co. Ltd.
SCOTIA (ATG) 87 1473 2097 79.02 10.91 3.91 10.0 gen(80c)
(launched as Meise)
Partenreederei m.s. "Rangiora"
WADDENS (ATG) 84 3784 5189 99.50 17.23 6.50 14.0 gen(350c)
(ex Southern Man-01, Capitaine Bligh-00, Waddens-99, Rangiora-98, Nedlloyd Trinidad-95,
Weser Guide-94, Zim Kingston-88, Weser Guide-84)

**Also larger ships and tankers ANCHORMAN, CHARTSMAN, RUDDERMAN and STEERSMAN,
which are managed by James Fisher (Shipping Services) Ltd.**

NORDSCHWEDEN FRACHTIENST GmbH VERWALTUNGSGESELLSCHAFT

Alana Shipping Co. Ltd.
ALANA (ATG) 99 2999 5049 95.16 13.17 6.06 12.0 gen(224c)
Saraco Shipping Co. Ltd.
ALEGRA (CYP) 97 2805 4241 89.90 13.17 5.68 12.5 gen(221c)
m.s. "Amira" Schiffahrtsges. mbH & Co. Reederei KG
AMIRA (NLD) 00 2999 5000 95.04 13.24 6.20 12.2 gen(213c)
Consailer Conship GmbH & Co. Reederei KG m.s. "Christina"
CHRISTINA (ATG) 98 2834 4743 89.78 13.27 6.22 12.0 gen(213c)
m.s. "Dania" Schiffahrtsges. mbH & Co. Reederei KG
DANIA (ATG) 00 2997 4956 94.96 13.17 6.20 12.0 gen(213c)
Conliner Conship GmbH & Co. Reederei KG m.s. "Esmeralda"
ESMERALDA (ATG) 98 2834 4616 89.78 13.27 6.12 12.0 gen(213c)
m.s. "Greta" Schiffahrtsges. mbH & Co. Reederei KG
GRETA (NLD) 99 2999 5000 95.04 13.24 6.20 12.2 gen(213c)
m.s. "Helena" Schiffahrtsges. mbH & Co. Reederei KG
HELENA (NLD) 99 2218 3400 89.40 12.50 5.15 12.0 gen
Alisma Shipping Co. Ltd.
ISABELLA (ATG) 98 2844 4618 89.78 13.27 6.21 12.0 gen(213c)
(ex Isabella I-01, launched as Isabella)
C. V. Lara
LARA (NLD) 98 3954 5727 100.85 14.95 6.50 13.7 gen(324c)
Nina Shipping C. V.
MELODY (NLD) 98 3954 5727 100.85 14.95 6.30 13.7 gen(324c)
(ex Nina-98)
m.s. "Rosa" Schiffahrtsges. mbH & Co. Reederei KG
ROSA (ATG) 00 2998 5050 95.16 13.17 6.18 12.2 gen(213c)
m.s. "Zara" Schiffahrtsges. mbH & Co. Reederei KG
ZARA (ANT) 00 2999 5050 95.16 13.26 6.20 12.2 gen(213c)

KLAUS-DIETER OELZE SCHIFFAHRTS KG

Reederei m.s. "Anke-Angela" Klaus-Dieter Oelze KG
ANKE-ANGELA
      (ATG) 84 1547 1910 82.48 11.38 3.72 10.7 gen(80c)
(ex Claudia Isabell-98)

JÜRGEN OHLE

Reederei Jurgen Ohle m.s. "Ragna"
BAUMWALL (DEU) 98 3999 5210 101.08 18.20 6.56 15.5 cc(508c)
(launched as Ragna)
Reederei Jurgen Ohle KG m.s. "Janra"
JANRA (DEU) 95 3999 5214 100.60 18.45 6.55 15.5 gen(508c)
m.s. "Dornbusch" Jurgen Ohle KG
NORRLAND (DEU) 96 3999 5220 101.10 18.45 6.56 15.5 gen(508c)
(launched as Dornbusch)
Also the larger SVEALAND.

CHRISTOPHER E. O. OPIELOK REEDEREI

m.s. "Christine O." Schiffahrtsges. mbH & Co. KG
CHRISTINE O. (DEU) 78 1925 2262 79.79 12.83 4.43 12.0 gen(145c)
(ex John Bluhm-98)

CLARA	(ATG)	75	1672	2130	75.77	11.82	4.67	11.0	gen(82c)

(ex Anita-95, Heide-Catrin-91)

m.s. "Marie O." Schiffahrtsges. mbH & Co. KG

SPAROS	(ATG)	79	2047	2515	86.67	12.83	4.87	13.5	gen(139c)

(launched as Inka)

"ORION" SCHIFFAHRTS-GESELLSCHAFT REITH & CO.

Fortuna Schiffahrtsges. mbH

MEKONG FORTUNE

	(ATG)	87	2610	2925	87.03	13.01	4.60	11.8	gen(153c)

(ex Saigon Fortune-96, Fortune Bay-92, Markham Bay-91, Magdalena R-88)

Orlanda Reederei GmbH

CAROLA	(ATG)	88	2610	2925	86.72	13.01	4.60	11.8	gen(153c)

(ex Tricolor Star II-96, Coringle Bay-91, Tiger Sea-90, Carola R-89)

Also larger ships.

CARL F. PETERS (GmbH & CO.)

Partenreederei m.s. "Eberhard"

EBERHARD	(ATG)	83	3075	5238	105.75	15.14	5.65	12.5	tk

Horst-Eberhard Eberhardt

PAUL	(CYP)	80	3003	5166	104.02	15.04	5.66	12.2	tk
WILLY	(CYP)	81	3070	5238	105.75	15.14	5.66	12.2	tk

(ex Gerhard-88)

Also larger ships.

On a rather overcast 23 August 1990, the **WILLY** heads up the Firth of Forth and approaches Grangemouth. (Bernard McCall)

JONNY PETERSEN
Partenreederei m.s. "Kerstin"
KERSTIN (ATG) 84 2683 3040 95.51 13.85 4.45 11.5 gen(166c)

PHOENIX REEDEREI GmbH
Polito Shipping Co. Ltd.
ADDI L. (GIB) 95 2876 4557 88.20 13.60 6.01 11.0 gen(173c)
(ex Blinke-98, Aspis-96)
Krey Schiffahrts GmbH & Co. m.s. "Hannah" KG
BBC COLUMBIA
(ATG) 87 3236 4257 99.42 14.05 5.44 12.5 gen(240c)
(ex Hannah-01, Paapsund-97, Paapsand-95, Sun Bay-95, Enno B-90, Myanmar Pioneer-92,
Tiger Cliff-91, Enno B-90, Nouakchott-90, Karin B-89, A.I.M. Voyager-87, launched as Karin B)
BOVENHUSEN (CYP)90 3186 4150 93.00 15.02 6.26 12.5 gen(180c)
(ex Southern Cross-00, Bartók-95)
Merridial Shipping Co. Ltd.
CARINA (CYP) 83 1988 2858 87.97 11.38 4.49 11.0 gen(72c)
(ex Intermare-97, Voga-94, Vänernsee-92)
m.s. "Christa K" Phoenix Reederei GmbH & Co. KG
CHRISTA K. (ATG) 89 1959 3015 87.70 12.50 4.61 11.0 gen(158c)
(ex Mindful-99, launched as Christian R)
Eglio Shipping Ltd
EMSTOR (CYP) 96 4180 4950 107.71 16.40 6.25 16.0 gen(408c)
(ex Maersk Castries-00, Maersk Maracaibo-98, Emstor-97)
Pavinco Shipping Ltd.
EVENBURG (CYP) 97 4135 5010 108.64 16.40 6.25 15.6 gen(408c)
(ex Maersk Coral-00, launched as Evenburg)
m.s. "Eversmeer" Phoenix Reederei GmbH & Co. KG
EVERSMEER (ATG) 90 2374 4161 88.29 13.21 5.74 12.0 gen
(ex Cady-97)
m.s. "Falderntor" Schiffahrts GmbH & Co. KG
FALDERNTOR (ATG) 95 3572 5027 96.71 15.82 6.20 13.5 gen(373c)
(ex Delmas Mahury-99, Ivaran Primero-97, Falderntor-96)
m.s. "Fockeburg" Schiffahrts GmbH & Co. KG
GLOBAL POWER
(ATG) 99 3821 5240 99.98 15.82 6.50 14.5 gen(375c)
(ex Global Africa-01, ex Global Power-00, ex Fockeburg-00)
Syntony Shipping Co. Ltd.
NESSE (CYP) 90 3186 4139 93.00 15.02 6.26 12.5 gen(180c)
(ex Wila Buck-98, FAS Colombo-97, Wila Buck-94)
Krey Schiffahrts GmbH & Co. m.s. "Sandwater" KG
SANDWATER (ATG) 93 1950 3036 88.30 12.50 4.64 11.6 gen(154c)
(ex Oxelösund-96, Sandwater-95)
Phoenix Reederei GmbH m.s. "Sirius P" KG
SIRIUS P (ATG) 90 2440 3181 87.47 13.02 4.83 12.0 gen(153c)
(ex Highland-99, Sirrah-95)
m.s. "Plytenberg" Schiffahrts GmbH & Co. KG
SOUTHERN AMELIA
(BHS) 91 3186 4146 93.00 15.02 5.80 12.5 gen(180c)
(ex Noumea Express-97, Nils R-97, launched as Kodaly)
Krey Schiffahrts GmbH & Co. m.s. "Svenja" KG
SVENJA (DEU) 96 2060 3000 88.45 11.40 4.95 gen(118c)

m.s. 'Ledator" Schiffahrts GmbH & Co.

TUXPAN REEF
        (ATG)   95   3458 5215   94.17 15.82   6.50 14.5 gen(375c)
    (ex Ledator-01, Dalmas Kourou-99, Delphine-97, Ledator-95)

Krey Schiffahrts GmbH & Co. m.s. "Wiebke K" KG

WIEBKE K (ATG)   94   1589 2735   82.50 11.55   4.80 10.0 gen(118c)

Also larger ships.

POHL SHIPPING SCHIFFAHRTSGESELLSCHAFT mbH

Partenreederei m.s. "Golf"

GOLF (DEU)   81   3060 3154   95.71 13.54   4.40 11.0 gen(118c)
    (ex Lyskraft-00, Golf-96)

Heinrich Kiepe Schiffahrts KG

HELJO (ATG)   93   2416 3574   84.95 13.03   5.44 11.5 gen(197c)
    (ex Hornsund-97, Heljo-96)

m.s. "Ness" Schiffahrtsgesellschaft Wilfried Jens KG

NESS (DEU)   96   3999 3881   100.15 15.50   5.48 14.5 gen(246c)

Also the larger ALTELAND.

WILHELM RAAP SCHIFFAHRTS KG

m.s. "Niederelbe" Raap Schiffahrts KG

NIEDERELBE (DEU) 82   1939 2890   87.97 11.38   4.67 11.0 gen(90c)

WILFRIED RAMBOW KG

m.s. "Gerda" Wilfried Rambow KG

GERDA (DEU)   95   3999 5300   100.60 18.45   6.56 15.5 gen(508c)

H. & W. Rambow m.s. "Ida Rambow" GmbH & Co. KG

IDA RAMBOW (DEU) 96   2863 4112   90.20 13.70   5.71 13.0 gen(261c)

m.s. "Vera" Wilfried Rambow KG

VERA (DEU)   96   3999 5207   101.11 18.45   6.55 15.5 gen(508c)

Also the larger LUCY BORCHARD.

RASS SCHIFFAHRTS GmbH & CO.

Partenreederei m.s. "Hoheweg" K.R. Ludwig Rass KG

HOHEWEG (DEU) 93   3992 5335   99.95 18.44   6.56 15.3 gen(515c)
    (ex Canarias-00, Hoheweg-98, OOCL Nevskiy-98, Hoheweg-98, Armada Reliance-95, Hoheweg-95)

Also the larger SUSAN BORCHARD and CHARLOTTE BORCHARD.

CARSTEN REHDER (GmbH & CO.)

Hans-Gustav Suhr

AROSETTE (ATG)   71   1205 1968   74.53 10.83   5.07 12.5 gen(63c)

Portishead Castle Shipping Co. Ltd.

BBC AMERICA (ATG) 99   4086 4806   100.60 16.60   5.80 15.0 gen(364c)
    (ex Bingum-99)

Schiffahrtsgesellschaft m.s. "Dora Mar" mbH & Co. KG

INDUSTRIAL BEACON
        (ATG)   91   3113 3487   92.70 15.12   5.32 12.0 gen
    (ex Bremer Makler-96, Gordon Reid-95)

Also larger ships.

REKA SHIPPING & CHARTERING GmbH
Bonus Shipping Co. Ltd.
BONUS (MLT) 74 2197 4017 82.23 13.37 6.61 9.2 gen(129c)
(ex Nimus-94, Rogall-93, Mattun-85, Gretchen-82, Gretchen Weston-82, Frendo Star-76)

RENCK & HESSENMULLER
Partenreederei m.s. "Ahrenshoop"
AHRENSHOOP
(DEU) 70 1641 1350 75.70 11.28 3.56 12.5 gen(74c)
(ex Frankto-78, Stokkfrakt-77, Frankto-75, Anglo Unity-74, Karen Oltmann-72)
Partenreederei m.s. "Ortrud"
ORTRUD (ATG) 78 1922 2995 95.03 11.41 4.70 12.5 gen(100c)
(ex Solveig-91, Pirat-87, Hip Pancevo-83, Pirat-81)

The timber deck cargo of the **AHRENSHOOP** is fully covered by tarpaulins as she heads up the Kieler Förde on 1 April 1999. (Dominic McCall)

SCHIFFAHRTSKONTOR RENDSBURG GmbH
Gebr. Mimietz KG
MAJA-M (PMD) 79 1624 1610 79.23 13.54 3.53 12.5 gen(142c)
Also larger ships.

RHEIN-MAAS UND SEE-SCHIFFAHRTSKONTOR GmbH
BWK Schiffinvest GmbH & Co. KG m.s. "RMS Duisburg"
RMS DUISBURG
(ATG) 83 1281 1572 74.91 10.60 3.38 10.2 gen
(ex Rhenus-98)
BWK Schiffinvest GmbH & Co. KG m.s. "RMS Mulheim"
RMS MULHEIM
(ATG) 99 1846 2500 89.74 11.67 4.48 13.0 gen(124c)

BWK Schiffinvest GmbH & Co. KG m.s. "RMS Ruhrort"
RMS RUHRORT
        (ATG)   83   1281 1566   74.88 10.60   3.38 10.2 gen
        (ex Amisia-98)
BWK Schiffinvest GmbH & Co. KG m.s. "RMS Voerde"
RMS VOERDE (ATG) 99   1846 2500   89.60 11.67   4.48 13.0 gen(124c)
BWK Schiffinvest GmbH & Co. KG m.s. "RMS Walsum"
RMS WALSUM (ATG) 84   1289 1450   74.91 10.60   3.39 10.0 gen
        (ex Mosa-98)

RHEIN-MAAS UND SEE-SCHIFFAHRSTKONTOR (HAMBURG) GmbH

m.s. "Euklid" Reederei KG Eidinger & Co.
EUKLID (ATG)   84   1860 3035   91.12 11.36   4.85 11.5 gen(67c)
        (ex Sena-94, Maelo-92, Zuiderzee-88)

When photographed in the Solent on 4 April 1995, the **EUKLID** had a blue hull. More recently, this has been changed to a light-grey colour, making a welcome change from the blue which characterises so many coasters.   (Chris Bancroft)

RHEIN-NORD-OSTSEE BEFRACHTUNGS GmbH

Shipcom Bereederungs GmbH & Co. Betriebs-KG m.s. "Albis"
ALBIS (ATG)   84   1781 2550   83.19 11.46   4.35 10.75 gen(72c)
        (ex Danubia-98)
Sea Dolphin Shipping Co. Ltd.
CRESCENT RHINE
        (ATG)   01   1900 2670   88.00 11.40   4.10 11.0 gen(84c)
Sea Whale Shipping Co. Ltd.
CRESCENT SEINE
        (ATG)   01   1900 2670   88.00 11.40   4.10 11.0 gen(84c)

KG m.s. "Elbia" Rhein-Nord-Ostsee Schiffahrtsges R. Boese & Co.
ELBIA   (CYP)   85   1525 1506   74.91   12.50   3.39 10.0 gen(84c)
Klaus Hülsermann KG m.s. "Maria H"
MARIA H   (ATG)   85   1297 1529   74.86   10.67   3.39 10.0 gen
ShipCom Bereederungs GmbH & Co. Betriebs-KG m.s. "Moldavia"
MOLDAVIA   (ATG)   85   1546 1708   82.48   11.38   3.51 10.5 gen(80c)
(ex Dania Carina-96)
ShipCom Bereederungs GmbH & Co. Betriebs-KG m.s. "Nemuna"
NEMUNA   (DEU)   98   2863 4139   89.70   13.60   5.71 13.0 gen(261c)
Thekla Schepers K.G. m.s. "Simone" & Co.
SIMONE   (DEU)   82   1710 2319   80.29   11.41   4.25 11.0 gen
ShipCom Bereederungs GmbH & Co. Betriebs-KG m.s. "Thamesis"
THAMESIS   (DEU)   97   2848 4186   90.50   13.60   5.73 13.0 gen(261c)
ShipCom Bereederungs GmbH & Co. Betriebs-KG m.s. "Visurgis"
VISURGIS   (DEU)   97   2835 4140   90.50   13.60   5.73 13.0 gen(261c)

HANS CARL RICKMERS
HELIOS II   (DEU) 64   385   485   44.52   7.57   2.91 9.0   gen

HANS RINCK BRENNSTOFFE OHG
GRETA   (DEU)   70   1126 1326   73.11   11.54   3.46 12.0 tk
(ex Bergen Nordic-97, Bjarkøy-97, Esso Bergen-95)

RIVER LINER BEFRACHTUNGS- UND BEREEDERUNGS GmbH
m.s. "Prag" Wessels River Liner KG
A. WETZEL   (DEU) 96   1043 1687   73.20   9.46   4.35 12.0 gen(63c)
(ex Prag-96)
m.s. "Carrier" River Liner GmbH & Co. KG
CARRIER   (CYP)   93   2514 3614   87.75   12.80   5.52 11.5 gen(168c)
(ex Seaprincess-99, Rügen-97)
Rudiger Fleig Schiffahrts KG m.s. "Clavigo"
CLAVIGO   (ATG)   92   2446 3735   87.90   12.89   5.50 10.6 gen(176c)
m.s. "Preussen" River Liner GmbH & Co. KG
FUNDO   (CYP)   95   989   1550   72.50   9.48   4.06 11.0 gen(62c)
(ex Preussen-95)
m.s. "Planet" River Liner GmbH & Co. KG
MCL EXPRESS
        (ATG)   99   3787 4625   93.30   16.50   6.25 14.5 gen(274c)
(ex Planet-01, Pannon Sky-00)
m.s. "Francia" Domhardt River Liner KG
MELANIE Z.   (CYP) 84   1289 1555   74.91   10.60   3.39 9.5   gen
(ex RMS Francia-98, Oranje Rotterdam-92, Sea Tamar-91)
m.s. "Moravia" CSPL River Liner GmbH & Co. KG
MORAVIA   (ATG)   01   1559 2500   83.16   10.95   4.72 12.0 gen
m.s. "Nordstern" Schepers River Liner KG
NORDSTERN   (ATG) 94   2446 3702   87.90   12.90   5.49 11.7 gen(176c)
m.s. "Pamir" River Liner GmbH & Co. KG
PAMIR   (CYP)   94   2061 3002   88.45   11.35   4.95 11.5 gen(118c)
m.s. "Parma" River Liner GmbH & Co. KG
PARMA   (ATG)   01   2999 4250   90.60   13.63   5.60 12.6 gen(122c)
m.s. "Parsival" River Liner GmbH & Co. KG
PARSIVAL   (CYP)   94   2061 3002   88.45   11.35   4.20 11.5 gen(118c)

m.s. "Pasadena" River Liner GmbH & Co. KG

PASADENA	(DEU)	01	1599					gen

m.s. "Peary" River Liner GmbH & Co. KG

PEARY	(ATG)	94	2514	3650	87.75	12.80	5.52	11.5	gen(168c)

(ex Larnaca Bay-99, Fischland-97)

The evening of 10 April 2001 saw four movements at the port of Fowey in Cornwall. One of two coasters to leave was the **PEARY**. (Dominic McCall)

m.s. "Pera" River Liner GmbH & Co. KG

PERA	(ATG)	95	2514	3596	87.90	12.80	4.50	12.0	gen(168c)

(ex Botsman Vlasov-95)

m.s. "Carrier" River Liner GmbH & Co. KG

PERLE	(DEU)	98	2981	4270	89.90	15.20	5.64	12.3	gen(114c)

m.s. "Peru" River Liner GmbH & Co. KG

PERU	(DEU)	98	2994	4280	90.60	15.20	5.64	12.3	gen(114c)

m.s. "Pex" CSPL River Liner GmbH & Co. KG

PEX	(DEU)	01	1599	2500	96.23	13.63	5.96	11.0	gen(114c)

m.s. "Plus" River Liner GmbH & Co. KG

PLUS	(DEU)	02	2993	4250	88.00	15.20	5.60	12.3	gen

m.s. "Podebrady" CSPL River Liner GmbH & Co. KG

PODEBRADY	(ATG)	99	1169	1857	78.30	9.46	4.35	12.0	gen(72c)

m.s. "Pola" River Liner GmbH & Co. KG

POLA	(CYP)	90	1690	1857	82.50	11.40	4.50	10.5	gen(84c)

(ex Heinke-98)

m.s. "Pommern" Wessels River Liner KG

POMMERN	(CYP)	94	2061	3006	88.45	11.35	4.95	11.5	gen(118c)

m.s. "Posen" River Liner GmbH & Co. KG

POSEN	(ATG)	93	2514	3560	87.75	12.80	5.52	11.5	gen(168c)

(ex Seaprogress-99, Usedom-97)

m.s. "Potosi" River Liner GmbH & Co. KG
POTOSI   (ATG)   95   2506   3657   87.90   12.80   4.50   12.0   gen(176c)
m.s. "Präsident" River Liner GmbH & Co. KG
PRÄSIDENT   (ATG)   95   2061   3004   88.49   11.35   4.95   11.5   gen(118c)
m.s. "Rheinfels" Domhardt River Liner KG
RHEINFELS   (ATG)   91   2381   3700   88.77   12.80   5.45   10.6   gen(176c)
m.s. "Tinsdal" Klaus Koss Schifahrts KG
TINSDAL   (DEU)   98   2981   4270   89.90   15.20   5.64   12.3   gen(114c)
m.s. "Pardubice" River Liner GmbH & Co. KG
WILSON MAAS
      (DEU)   97   1169   1850   78.30   9.46   4.35   12.0   gen(70c)
(ex Pardubice-01)
m.s. "Lovosice" CSPL River Liner GmbH & Co. KG
WILSON RHINE
      (DEU)   98   1171   1832   78.30   9.46   4.35   12.0   gen(72c)
(ex Lovosice-00)
m.s. "Pilsen" River Liner GmbH & Co. KG
WILSON RUHR
      (DEU)   97   1169   1826   73.20   9.46   4.35   12.0   gen(63c)
(ex Pilsen-01)
m.s. "Wittenbergen" Koss River Liner KG
WITTENBERGEN
      (CYP)   92   2381   3700   87.90   12.80   5.45   10.6   gen(176c)

RMS LÜBECK SCHIFFAHRTS GmbH
Dirks Shipping Co. Ltd.
HANNES D   (ATG)   68   1037   1200   68.43   10.52   4.30   12.5   gen
(ex Windö-98, Mjovik-91, Windö-90, Nincop-88)
Lotthar Frank
IRLO   (ATG)   69   1208   1964   74.02   10.83   5.06   12.5   gen(63c)
(ex Anta-94, Simone-89, Tina-76)
Reederei Robert & Ursula Busse
JESSICA   (DEU)   65   530   584   47.81   8.82   3.06   10.0   gen
(ex Freiheit-91, Silja-78, Kahlenberg-77, Regina-71)
URSULA B   (ATG)   64   1011   1185   66.20   10.57   3.96   11.0   gen
(ex Neuenfelde-95, Eduard Kähler-87, Heinrich Knüppel-71)
Balhon Shipping S. de R. L.
JOLANDA   (HND)   56   499   964   57.84   8.97   3.52   10.5   gen
(ex Svend Dammann-89, Robox-69)
Largo Shipping S. de R. L.
LARGO II   (HND)   73   299   711   49.71   8.34   3.47   11.0   gen
(ex Janie-89, Sterno-84, Saralil-79)
LARGONA   (VCT)   76   866   1195   63.71   10.62   3.98   12.0   gen
(ex Biscay Spirit-95, Irino-87)
Drabert Schiffahrts GmbH
MINCHEN D   (ATG)   78   1768   1964   72.29   12.83   4.45   12.5   gen(127c)
(ex Schulau-00)
WIEBKE D   (ATG)   80   1441   1795   80.96   11.33   3.29   10.5   gen
(ex Pandor-97)
Mistral Shipping Co. Ltd.
MISTRAL   (ATG)   66   1064   1196   68.36   10.55   3.96   11.0   gen
(ex Nadine-98, Ragna-90, Tilla-93, Süderelv-78, Frieda Graebe-73)

Coast Trade S. de R. L.
TONJA (HND) 57 499 864 53.68 7.84 3.91 10.0 gen
(ex Salona-86, Samstein-76, Falstein I-70, Tonja-69)

RMS SCHIFFAHRSTKONTOR BREMEN GmbH
Fritz & Falco Kohiken Kusten- u. Seeschiffahrt
HERA (DEU) 75 1202 1300 74.99 10.24 3.31 10.5 gen
(ex Herm Kiepe-96)
Also the larger PAMPERO.

ROHDEN BEREEDERUNG GmbH & CO. KG
AGENA (ATG) 01 2528 3380 86.40 12.80 5.56 11.5 gen(167c)
(launched as Offshore II)
m.s. "Apus" Rohden Schiffahrts GmbH & Co. KG
APUS (ATG) 90 2642 3100 89.99 13.00 4.60 12.0 gen(198c)
(ex Anke Ehler-98)
m.s. "Aquila" GmbH & Co. KG
AQUILA (ATG) 00 2528 3380 86.40 12.80 5.56 12.3 gen(167c)
(ex Offshore I-00, launched as Eemnes)
m.s. "Coronel" Rohden Schiffahrts GmbH & Co. KG
CORONEL (ATG) 78 2089 2461 86.64 12.83 4.87 13.3 gen(195c)
(ex Lys Coronel-00, Coronel-97, Christel-85)
m.s. "Dorado" R.S.T. Schiffahrts GmbH & Co. KG
DORADO (ATG) 98 3862 4974 100.70 16.40 6.25 16.0 gen(406c)
(ex Echo Trader-00, Seaboard Enterprise-00, Echo Trader-99)
m.s. "Grus" Rohden Schiffahrts GmbH & Co. KG
GEEST ATLAS (ATG) 96 2906 3950 99.45 16.44 5.04 15.5 cc(340c)
(ex Bell Atlas-97)
m.s. "Pavo" Rohden Schiffahrts GmbH & Co. KG
NORMED ISTANBUL
(ATG) 86 3300 4107 92.44 15.70 6.36 13.7 gen(321c)
(ex Pavo-00, Seevetal-98)
m.s. "Tucana" Rohden Schiffahrts GmbH & Co. KG
TUCANA (ATG) 85 2732 3900 89.80 14.19 6.32 12.8 gen(203c)
(ex Rangitikei-96, Lisa Heeren-92, Santa Paula-90, Lisa Heeren-89, Band Aid II-85,
Lisa Heeren-85)
Also larger ships.

REEDEREI HANS AUGUST SABBAN
BIRGIT SABBAN
(DEU) 84 2119 3042 92.11 11.54 4.71 11.0 gen(100c)
Partenreederei m.s. "Marlies Sabban"
MARLIES SABBAN
(DEU) 86 2120 3028 92.11 11.54 4.70 10.0 gen(100c)
(ex Petra-Gunda-95)

KAPITÄN HANS BERND SCHEPERS
HS Schiffahrts GmbH & Co. KG m.s. "Sea Ems"
SEA EMS (ATG) 84 1857 2200 80.73 12.70 4.17 10.5 gen(102c)
(ex Gatje-00, Gama-98, Lys Captain-96, Gama-95)
HS Schiffahrts GmbH & Co. KG m.s. "Johanna"
SEA WAAL (ATG) 85 1843 2325 80.02 12.70 4.17 10.5 gen(102c)
(ex Triton Navigator-01, Lys Crown-99, Ettina-97)

RUDOLF SCHEPERS

Rudolf Schepers KG m.s. "Christopher"

CHRISTOPHER
(DEU)   90   2292 2690   84.90 12.90   4.43 11.0 gen(129c)

Also the larger BORUSSIA DORTMUND.

REEDEREI THEKLA SCHEPERS GmbH & Co. KG

TESCH Bereederungsgesellschaft mbH & Co. KG m.s. "Katharina B"

KATHARINA B (DEU) 97   3995 5865   99.95 17.90   6.60 16.5 cc(520c)

TESCH Bereederungsgesellschaft mbH & Co. KG m.s. "Margarita B"

MARGARETA B
(DEU)   98   3999 5865   99.95 17.90   6.60 16.0 cc(520c)
(ex Pacific Transporter-98, Margareta B-98)

TESCH Bereederungsgesellschaft mbH & Co. KG m.s. "Thea B"

THEA B (DEU)   95   2899 3950   99.33 16.20   4.90 14.5 gen(340c)
(ex Bell Astron-97, launched as Thea B)

TESCH Bereederungsgesellschaft mbH & Co. KG m.s. "Verena B"

VERENA B (DEU)   92   3958 5356   107.98 16.50   5.99 15.2 gen(448c)
(ex Aquitaine Star-98, Verena B-97)

The **THEA B** arrives at Aberdeen on 15 July 2001. She is the regular vessel on the Concorde container service linking the Scottish ports of Aberdeen and Grangemouth to Antwerp. This Sunday arrival was unusual as she normally arrives in Aberdeen on a Friday.   (David Dodds)

REEDEREI KARL SCHLÜTER GmbH & CO. KG

KG m.s. "Betsy" Schiffahrtsges. mbH & Co.

BETSY (DEU)   98   2986 4830   98.43 16.90   5.91 14.5 cc(366c)

KG m.s. "Heike" Schiffahrtsges. mbH & Co.

HEIKE (DEU)   98   2986 4830   98.43 16.90   5.91 14.5 cc(366c)

KG m.s. "Henny" Schiffahrtsgesellschaft mbH & Co.

HENNY	(DEU)	97	2986	4830	98.43	16.90	5.91	14.5	cc(366c)

KG m.s. "Ute" Schiffahrtsges. mbH & Co.

UTE	(DEU)	99	2988	4830	98.43	16.90	5.91	14.5	cc(366c)

Also larger ships.

WILHELM E. F. SCHMID GmbH

Norbert u. Dr. Axel Meyer

BJÖRN M	(DEU)	55	328	480	47.60	8.54	2.68	9.0	gen

(ex Traute-86)

THOMAS M.	(DEU)	61	225	378	41.31	7.29	2.85	8.5	gen

(ex Hille-83)

Anke Iwersen-Kreetz

DIDE	(DEU)	1901	207	310	38.59	6.86	2.13	7.0	gen

(ex Gesa-66, Grauerort-65, Vier Gebroeders)

Nahmen Christiansen

NATALIE	(DEU)	50	475	681	58.77	7.52	3.16	8.5	gen

(ex Margot Schlichting-01, Elli Ahrens-71)

Despite being over fifty years old, the **NATALIE** is in superb condition. She was photographed as she entered the Kieler Förde from the Baltic on 4 July 2001. (Oliver Sesemann)

NORDLAND I	(DEU)	62	269	389	41.94	7.57	2.43	8.5	gen

(ex Helena K-89, Braker Wappen-78, Nordhelm-75)

RENATE	(DEU)	52	499	774	58.86	7.52	3.36	9.0	gen

(ex Cum Deo-96, Süderelbe-89, Renate-62)

Karl Meyer Umweltdienste GmbH

HELGOLAND	(DEU)	55	492	632	54.08	8.03	2.84	8.0	gen

(ex Kaja H-98, Gauensiek-86, Whitte Kliff-71, Marschenland-65)

NEULAND	(DEU)	66	494	500	53.24	8.44	3.06	9.5	gen

(ex Lilly K-96, Adele J-78)

Jens Boysen
STEENBORG (DEU) 67   718 1080   54.97   9.63   3.35 8.7 gen
(ex Berta Morgenroth-81)
Reinhold Fischer KG
UTE (DEU)   84   1520 1837   76.45 11.46   3.86 10.0 gen

WOLFGANG SCHMIDT
Fahrdorfer Schiffahrts GmbH & Co. m.s. "Merit"
MERIT (GIB)   00   2301 3171   82.50 12.60   5.30 12.0 gen(132c)
m.s. "Mermaid" Eicke Schiffahrts KG
MERMAID (MLT)   85   1856 2302   80.73 12.65   4.18 10.5 gen(102c)

SEAVOSS SCHIFFAHRT GmbH
m.s. "Angelburg" Voss Schiffahrts KG
ANGELBURG (ATG) 81   1939 2890   87.97 11.30   4.67 11.0 gen(70c)
(ex Margaretha-96)
m.s. "Asseburg" Voss Schiffahrts KG
ASSEBURG (ATG)   82   1939 2890   87.97 11.54   4.67 11.0 gen(90c)
(ex Catharina-96)
m.s. "Breitenburg" Voss Schiffahrts KG
BREITENBURG
(ATG)   82   1939 2890   87.97 11.33   4.67 11.5 gen(90c)
(ex Keitum-95, Jule-94, Balder-93, Jule-88)
m.s. "Kaaksburg" Voss Schiffahrts KG
KAAKSBURG (ATG) 81   1939 2889   87.97 11.33   4.67 11.5 gen(90c)
(ex Torex-95, Tini-95, Loke-93, Tini-88)
m.s. "Paaschburg" Hans Voss KG
PAASCHBURG (ATG) 80   3228 3996   93.30 14.47   5.78 14.0 gen(263c)
(ex Borstel-97, Jupiter-93, Iberian Bridge-93, Jupiter-92, ECL Cadet-92, Clipper-91,
Manchester Clipper-80, launched as Clipper)
m.s. "Schulenburg" Voss Schiffahrts KG
SCHULENBURG
(CYP)   81   2265 2976   99.80 11.41   4.34 10.5 gen(100c)
(ex Ursula-96, Ursula Wessels-90)
m.s. "Steinburg" Voss Schiffahrts KG
STEINBURG (ATG) 82   1939 2885   87.97 11.33   4.68 11.5 gen(90c)
(ex Comet-95)
m.s. "Treuburg" Kommanditgesellschaft
TREUBURG (ATG)   83   1939 2888   87.97 11.54   4.67 11.5 gen(90c)
(ex Sea Weser-99)
m.s. "Trotzenburg" Voss Schiffahrts KG
TROTZENBURG
(ATG)   82   1988 2857   88.04 11.38   4.49 11.0 gen(72c)
(ex Sarah-00, Saga-95, Saimaasee-92)

SEE-TRANSIT BEREEDERUNGS GmbH
Seetransit Bereederungs GmbH & Co. KG m.s. "Petersburg"
PETERSBURG (ATG) 85   1838 2285   80.60 12.70   4.17 11.0 gen(96c)
(ex Peter S-93)
Seetransit Bereederungs GmbH & Co. KG m.s. "Rhine Liner"
RHINE-LINER (ATG) 78 2319 2851   99.73 11.41   4.12 10.7 gen(104c)
(ex Rhone-Liner-92, Smederovo-82, Rhone Liner-81)
Also the larger CONRO TRADER.

REEDEREI BERND SIBUM GmbH & Co. KG
m.s. "Gerd Sibum" Schiffahrts GmbH & Co. KG
GERD SIBUM (ATG) 98   3999 5272   99.95 17.90   6.60 16.0 cc(5233c)
(ex Maersk Salerno-99, Gerd Sibum-98)
Also larger ships.

KURT SIEMER
Stephanie Coast Shipping Co. Ltd.
KATHARINA SIEMER
           (CYP)   85   2061 3357   87.99 11.54   5.24 11.0 gen(90c)
(ex Katharina S-99, RMS Hispana-95, Katharina Siemer-93)
STEPHANIE S. (CYP) 80   1751 2422   85.68 11.38   3.95 10.75 gen(90c)
(ex RMS Lettia-96, Stephanie Siemer-93)

SLOMAN-NEPTUN SCHIFFAHRTS-AG
Partenreederei m.s. "Sloman Royal"
ALEGRE FEEDER
           (ATG)   83   4291 3641   92.39 18.14   4.45 12.5 gen/ro(278c)
(ex Spirit of Progress-98, Mareike-93, Dorcas-93, Mareike-90, Sloman Royal-88)
Deltagas Shipping Co. Ltd.
DELTAGAS (LBR)   92   3011 3582   88.35 14.22   6.21 14.5 lpg
Gammagas Shipping Co. Ltd.
GAMMAGAS (LBR)   92   3703 4447   99.35 15.02   6.47 14.8 lpg
Lingegas Shipping NV
LINGEGAS (ANT)   81   2700 3403   82.56 14.10   6.50 13.5 lpg
Merwegas Shipping NV
MERWEGAS (ANT)   81   2712 3403   82.56 14.10   6.50 13.5 lpg
Omegagas Shipping Co Ltd.
OMEGAGAS (ATG)   99   3366 3650   95.60 14.40   6.25 14.0 lpg
Regent Shipping Co. Ltd.
SLOMAN REGENT
           (ATG)   82   3922 2561   91.95 18.14   4.21 12.2 gen/ro(260c)
Rider Shipping Co. NV
SLOMAN RIDER
           (ATG)   79   3887 2570   91.95 18.14   4.21 12.5 gen/ro(319c)
Rover Shipping Co. Ltd.
SLOMAN ROVER
           (ATG)   79   4298 3530   92.41 18.42   4.55 12.0 gen/ro(269c)
(ex Buxsand-94, Heinrich S-94, Calypso I-85, Heinrich S-85, launched as Paoua)
Also larger ships.

SOHL SCHIFFAHRT VERWALTUNGS GmbH
Burmester Shipping Ltd.
GUADALUPE 2
           (CYP)   86   1899 2295   82.10 12.65   4.17 11.0 gen(147c)
(ex Lys Corona-97, Sprante-96, launched as Emma)
Brodersen Shipping Ltd.
PIA (CYP)   85   1720 1710   81.11 12.70   3.45 10.0 gen(112c)
(ex Käthe Prahm-96)

REEDEREI MARTIN SPALECK
Reliant Shipping Co. Ltd.
MARLIN (ATG)   79   2354 2604   84.26 13.54   4.92 14.0 gen(172c)
(ex Reliant-93, Johanna-91)

CLAUS SPECK GmbH

Gerina Shipping Co. Ltd.
ANUND (CYP)   75   2240 2750   81.39   13.42   5.03 13.0 gen(149c)
(ex Odin-84, Eco Liz-83, Odin-81)

m.s. "Frej" Claus-Markus Speck KG
FREJ (ATG)   94   2997 4470   97.27   16.15   5.93 14.8 gen(304c)

Claus Markus Speck KG
HOLSTEIN (DEU)   91   3815 4660   103.50 16.24   6.70 14.5 gen(372c)
(ex Gracechurch Planet-96, Nordic Bridge-94, ECL Commander-91, Schleswig-Holstein-91)

Grade Universe Shipping Co. Ltd.
JORUND (CYP)   76   2240 2560   81.39   13.44   5.04 14.0 gen(150c)
(ex Seefalke-85)

m.s. "Odin" Claus-Markus Speck KG
ODIN (ATG)   94   2997 4530   97.27   16.15   5.93 14.7 gen(304c)

JURGEN STAHMER

Partenreederei m.s. "Jan"
BLUE SKY (ATG)   84   3120 3676   88.63   15.47   6.45 12.0 gen(256c)
(ex Mandeb Bay-98, Blue Sky-95, Saigon Lotus-93, Blue Sky-93, Carme-90, Inka Dede-90, Regency Bay-87, Inka Dede-87)

REEDEREI STEFFENS GmbH & Co. KG

m.s. "Wilhelmine Steffens" Reederei Steffens GmbH & Co. KG
WILHELMINE STEFFENS
           (DEU)   81   1022 1092   74.33   9.53   2.91 10.0 gen
(ex RMS Scotia-92, Wilhelmine Steffens-92, Lucky Star-91)

The **WILHELMINE STEFFENS** was photographed at Goole on 17 February 2000. She had arrived from Perth that day and sailed later to Bremen. (Richard Potter)

KAPITÄN FRANK STOLZENBERGER
ARNGAST (DEU) 58 833 1030 61.14 10.06 3.80 10.2 gen
(ex Beta-97, Drochtersen-91, Baltica-75, Weser-64)

E. STRAHLMANN SCHIFFAHRTSVERWALTUNG
Edwin Strahlmann m.s. "Alexandra"
ALEXANDRA 76 2245 2565 81.41 13.44 5.03 13.75 gen (162c)
(ex Cuxhaven-00)

Three months after coming into the Erwin Strahlmann fleet, the **ALEXANDRA** approaches the new south lock at Kiel on 9 September 2000. (Oliver Sesemann)

Partenreederei m.s. "Anjola"
ANJOLA (ATG) 77 1519 2143 74.02 11.99 3.98 9.5 gen(68c)
(ex RMS Polonia-94, Anjola-92)
Estra Shipping Ltd
AZUR (ATG) 81 1826 3080 81.92 11.38 5.01 11.0 gen(63c)
(ex Nordfahrt-95)
Afran Horizon Shipping Co Ltd
BOUNDER (ATG) 86 1984 3223 89.31 12.51 4.70 11.5 gen(148c)
(ex Borsteler Berg-97, Hetlo-94, Borsteler Berg-92)
Partenreederei m.s. Christian
CHRISTIAN (ATG) 77 2089 2461 86.49 12.83 4.85 13.2 gen(195c)
(ex Alita-95)
Edwin Strahlmann m.s. "Dealer"
DEALER (ATG) 82 1662 2318 80.32 11.38 4.25 10.5 gen
(Lena-S-01)
A/S Urting
DREDGER (ATG) 79 1512 1809 82.45 11.41 3.56 10.5 gen(48c)
(ex Falko-01, Marne-95, Sea Elbe-94, launched as Christa Schütt)

Edwin Strahlmann m.s. "Elsebeth"
ELSEBETH (ATG) 86 1636 2280 82.48 11.31 4.23 10.5 gen(44c)
(ex Sea Elbe-01, Silke-95)
Erwin Diedrich Strahlmann
GAMBLER (ATG) 79 2319 2920 99.73 11.41 4.21 11.0 gen(104c)
(ex Timor-98, Käthe-96, Käthe Wessels-90)
Helse Shipping Ltd
HELSE (ATG) 92 1582 1900 81.20 11.39 3.60 11.0 gen(75c)
(launched as Hanse Carrier)
Erwin Strahlmann m.s. "Hunter"
HUNTER (ATG) 81 1939 2890 87.97 11.36 4.67 11.5 gen(90c)
(ex Deike-98)
Afran Ocean Shipping Co Ltd
JUMPER (ATG) 90 1960 2999 89.03 12.50 4.57 11.5 gen(158c)
(ex Karibu-97, Petra-95)
Partenreederei m.s. "Konigsberg"
KORALLE (ATG) 85 1851 2269 80.02 12.70 4.18 10.5 gen(142c)
(ex RMS Hollandia-94, Koralle-92)
m.s. "Marek" Strahlmann Schiffahrts KG
MAREK (ATG) 83 1999 3345 88.04 11.38 4.49 11.0 gen(72c)
(ex Elly Bojen-95)
m.s. "Mike" Strahlmann Schiffahrts KG
MIKE (ATG) 82 1513 1721 82.45 11.38 4.22 10.7 gen(48c)
(ex Patria-94)
m.s. "Performer" Strahlmann Schiffahrts KG
PERFORMER (ATG) 87 1392 1570 71.96 11.51 3.58 11.0 gen(69c)
(ex Piano-99, Süllberg-88)
Partenreederei m.s. "Provider"
PROVIDER (ATG) 81 1834 2623 78.59 12.83 4.60 10.25 gen(88c)
(ex Ruthensand-00, Echo Trader-90, Ruthensand-87)
Partenreederei m.s. "Beaver"
RMS LAGUNE (ATG) 82 1059 1150 74.17 9.86 2.92 10.0 gen(60c)
(ex RMS Normandia-93, Lagune-93)
Partenreederei m.s. "Karen E"
RMS WESTFALIA
(ATG) 80 1059 1173 74.17 9.86 2.92 10.0 gen(60c)
(ex Karin E-92, Atoll-92)
Partenreederei m.s. "Roger"
ROGER (ATG) 84 1520 2183 82.48 11.38 4.05 10.5 gen(80c)
(ex Gudrun-92, Aros Anglia-92, Gudrun-90)
Erwin Strahlmann m.s. "Sprinter"
SPRINTER (DEU) 77 2372 2720 84.26 13.52 4.96 14.0 gen(149c)
(ex Theodor Storm-00, Somers Isles-99, Theodor Storm-85, Baltic Heron-83,
Theodor Storm-78)
Partenreederei m.s. "Susanna"
SUSANNA (ATG) 80 1499 1561 82.48 11.38 3.56 10.5 gen(48c)
(ex Anke Bettina-00, Pelikan-92, Hammaburg-89)
m.s. "Trdaer" Strahlmann Schiffahrts KG
TRADER (ATG) 80 1527 1782 82.48 11.38 3.56 10.5 gen(80c)
(ex Cranz II-01, Cranz-98, Matthias-93, Vuoksi-91, Matthias-91, Echo Matthias-90, Elbe-89)
Partenreederei m.s. "Urte"
URTE (ATG) 76 2551 2908 96.32 12.45 5.48 11.5 gen(207c)
(ex Ulzburg-96, Urte-94, Katterpel-90, Neuwulmstorf II-87, Neuwulmstorf-86)

Andreas Petersen KG

VIPER   (ATG)   86   1587   2380   82.02   11.49   4.21   10.0   gen
   (ex Lisa-01, Edith-90, Echo Lisa-89, Edith-89)

Afran River Shipping Ltd.

WALKER   (ATG)   86   1392   1570   71.96   11.51   3.27   11.0   gen(69c)
   (ex Petersberg-98, Echo Elke-91, Petersberg-89)

Also the larger ZIM VENEZUELA I.

SUNSHIP SCHIFFAHRTSKONTOR KG

Reederei M. Lauterjung m.s. "Arion" KG

ARION   (ATG)   98   1846   2500   89.60   11.65   4.45   13.0   gen(124c)

Reederei M. Lauterjung m.s. "Berit L" KG

BERIT L.   (ATG)   88   1307   1538   74.90   10.60   3.37   11.5   gen

Reederei M. Lauterjung GmbH & Co. KG Sunship Eurocoaster m.s. "Delia"

DELIA   (ATG)   00   1846   2500   89.60   11.67   4.48   13.0   gen(126c)

Giemow & Sohne KG m.s. "Gorch Foch"

GORCH FOCH   (ATG) 86   1525   1506   74.33   12.43   3.28   10.0   gen(84c)

Reederei M. Lauterjung m.s. "Hestia" KG

HESTIA   (ATG)   99   1599   2500   89.60   11.67   4.45   13.0   gen(124c)

Reederei Helms-Niessen m.s. "Jerome H" KG

JEROME H.   (ATG)   85   1297   1525   74.91   10.60   3.67   10.0   gen

Reederei M. Lauterjung m.s. "Kay L" KG

KAY L   (DEU)   84   1298   1537   74.91   10.60   3.32   10.0   gen

Fully laden with a cargo of scrap metal destined for a northern Spanish port, the **KAY L** leaves
St Sampsons harbour, Guernsey, on 20 April 1998.   (Tony Rive)

Arpa Shipping m.s. "Marcel" Schiffahrts GmbH & Co. KG

MARCEL   (ATG)   93   2449   3710   87.85   12.50   5.45   10.0   gen(180c)

Reederei M. Lauterjung m.s. "Jupiter" KG

MSC BAHAMAS
   (ATG)   91   2450   3710   87.85   12.81   5.47   10.0   gen(180c)
   (ex Jupiter-00)

Tramp Ship Eight Co. Ltd.
NESTOR   (ATG)   00   1846 2500   89.60   11.65   4.49 13.0 gen(126c)
Reederei M. Lauterjung m.s. "Richard C" KG
RICHARD C.   (ATG)   84   1298 1537   74.91   10.60   3.32 10.0 gen
(ex RMS Anglia-99, Richard C.-98)
Reederei M. Lauterjung m.s. "Saturn" KG
SATURN   (ATG)   92   2449 3710   87.85   12.81   5.47 11.0 gen(180c)
(ex MSC Bahamas-00, Saturn-97)
Reederei M. Lauterjung m.s. "Sunrise" KG
SUNRISE   (ATG)   92   2449 3678   87.85   12.81   5.47 10.0 gen(180c)
(ex Stadt Wilhelmshaven-92, launched as Castor)
Tramp Ship Six Co. Ltd.
THEBE   (ATG)   00   1847 2500   89.60   11.65   4.45 13.0 gen(124c)
Tramp Ship Seven Co. Ltd.
THESEUS   (ATG)   00   1846 2500   89.60   11.65   4.45 13.0 gen(124c)
Reederei M. Lauterjung m.s. "Uranus" KG
URANUS   (ATG)   92   2449 3710   87.55   12.81   5.46 11.0 gen(180c)
Tramp Ship Five Co. Ltd.
ZEUS   (ATG)   99   1599 2500   89.60   11.70   4.45 13.0 gen(124c)
Also larger ships.

HOLGER UND HERBERT SZIDAT KG

m.s. "Holger" Holger und Herbert Szidat KG
HOLGER   (CYP)   95   3999 5207   101.15   18.45   6.56 15.5 gen(508c)
(ex UB Lion-97, Holger-95)
m.s. "Jana" Holger und Herbert Szidat KG
SOMERS ISLES
      (ATG)   90   3125 3070   89.60   16.16   4.80 14.6 gen(260c)
(ex Jana-99)

REEDEREI RAINER TEGTMEIER

Reederei Rainer Tegtmeier m.s. "Henning S" KG
HENNING S.   (ATG)   89   1307 1739   74.90   10.60   3.66 10.2 gen
Reederei Rainer Tegtmeier m.s. "Werder Bremen" KG
WERDER BREMEN
      (ATG)   85   1297 1529   74.91   10.60   3.39 10.0 gen

THIEN & HEYENGA BEREEDERUNGS- UND BEFRACHTUNGS GmbH

Warfer Schiffahrts GmbH & Co. KG
BORGFELD   (ATG)   85   2881 4168   99.80   14.64   5.24 11.0 gen(174c)
Kalafia Ltd.
CALAFIA   (BHS)   79   2989 3550   101.93   14.46   5.35 14.0 ref
(ex Azteca-95, Calafia-92)
Transice Marine Co. Ltd.
DAKOTA   (CYP)   77   2989 3507   101.94   14.46   9.88 14.0 ref
(ex Jan Mayen-92, Jan Willem-90)
Interice Marine Co. Ltd.
INCA   (CYP)   78   2989 3536   101.94   14.46   4.75 14.0 ref
N.V. Shipping Co. Oceanice
LIMA   (ANT)   79   2989 2510   103.00   14.46   5.30 14.0 ref
(ex Mathilda-92)

Neerlandic NTH Shipping Ltd.
NEERLANDIC (ATG) 85 3955 5232 108.77 16.34 7.35 16.0 ref(93c)
Arcadian Sky Shipping Co. Ltd.
P & O NEDLLOYD GIZAN
(CYP) 94 3978 5273 104.75 16.57 6.55 16.0 gen(373c)
(ex Arcadian Sky-00, Frontier America-97)
m.s. "Stadt Norden" Fresa Schiffahrtsbeiteiligungs-GmbH & Co. KG
SOUTHERN EXPRESS
(ATG) 86 2800 2985 85.55 15.24 4.40 11.0 gen(246c)
(ex Wilstedt-01, Nouakchott-00, Eembay-99, Stadt Norden-98, FLS America-97, Stadt
Norden-97, Cafe Express-93, Stadt Norden-92, Delmas Zaire-90, Stadt Norden-90)
m.s. "Stadt Cuxhaven" Schiffahrts GmbH & Co. KG
STADT CUXHAVEN
(DEU) 96 4004 5243 104.75 16.40 6.62 16.0 gen(375c)
(ex Ivaran Segundo-98, Stadt Cuxhaven-97)
Arcadian Faith Shipping Co. Ltd.
STADT HANNOVER
(CYP) 94 3978 5573 104.75 16.57 6.55 16.0 gen(373c)
(ex Arcadian Faith-01, FLS Colombia-97, Arcadian Faith-94)
m.s. "Stadt Kiel" NTH Schiffahrts GmbH & Co. KG
STADT KIEL (DEU) 96 3978 5273 104.75 16.40 6.63 16.0 gen(373c)
(ex Eagle Caribe-97, Stadt Kiel-96)
m.s. "Tarmstedt" NTH Schiffahrts GmbH & Co. KG
TARMSTEDT (ATG) 85 2800 2980 85.55 15.24 4.40 11.0 gen(246c)
(ex Eemlagune-00, Stadt Leer-99, Valiant-97, Stadt Leer-91)
Also larger ships.

JOHS. THODE GmbH & CO.
Wolfgang & Carsten Kleige Partenreederei m.s. "Charlotte"
CHARLOTTE (ATG) 69 1440 1477 77.20 11.84 4.04 11.0 gen(72c)
(ex Hinrich Behrmann-89, Tweed-70, launched as Hinrich Behrmann)
Reederei Kapitan Uwe Kruse m.s. "Navigia"
NAVIGIA (DEU) 75 2240 2560 81.39 13.42 5.03 13.7 gen(149c)
(ex DFL Hamburg-94, Dana Navigia-90, Navigia-90, Donar-79)
Also larger ships.

HEINRICH THORDSEN K.G.
Reederei Thordsen m.s. "Elisabeth" KG
ELISABETH (DEU) 83 1139 1102 63.02 11.33 3.27 9.8 gen(43c)
Reederei Thordsen m.s. "Ilka" KG
ILKA (DEU) 85 1366 1300 71.81 11.33 3.23 10.0 gen
Reederei Thordsen m.s. "Irmgard" KG
IRMGARD (DEU) 81 1139 1113 63.02 11.31 3.27 10.0 gen(43c)
Reederei Thordsen m.s. "Maike" KG
MAIKE (DEU) 89 1599 1908 82.00 11.48 3.68 10.0 gen

m.s. "THULE" SCHIFFAHRTSGES. mbH & Co. KG
THULE (DEU) 96 2771 4140 90.50 13.60 5.71 13.0 gen(261c)

WILHELM TIETJEN BEFRACHTUNGES. mbH
J. T. M. Shipping Co. Ltd.
JAMAL (VCT) 77 1592 3256 91.52 13.31 5.14 12.5 gen(60c)
(ex Leszek G-00, Leslie Gault-92)

TALAL (VCT) 78 2025 3070 85.32 13.75 4.99 12.0 gen
    (ex Redthorn-01, Pinewood-90)
H.C. Shipping Co. Ltd.
KABAN (ATG) 71 2900 5644 85.42 15.30 7.45 11.5 gen
    (ex Kawan-97, Mirka-92, Mara-90, Mawan-87, Bohol-83, Saint Nazaire-81)
LGM Shipping Co. Ltd.
LINACO (ATG) 72 2863 5656 85.83 15.30 7.45 10.75 gen
    (ex Lina-97, Sainan-90, Hamburg-85)
MALANGA (ATG) 71 2900 5656 85.83 15.30 7.45 10.75 gen
    (ex Alan-97, Malanga-87, Geneve-85)
Mona Rosa Shipping Co. Ltd.
MONA ROSA (ATG) 77 1595 2820 81.44 11.94 4.78 11.5 gen(84c)
    (ex Stepenitz-99, Noordland-89)

On 3 September 2000, the **MONA ROSA** is about to berth at Gunness Wharf on the River Trent at the end of a voyage from Safi. (David Dixon)

TRANSOCEAN SHIPMANAGEMENT GmbH
Navegar Comphanhia Portugesa de Navegacao International S.A.
ALCOA CHEMIST
    (PMD) 92 2634 3743 90.00 14.49 6.15 14.0 ch tk
    (ex Annette Essberger-97)
DOURO CHEMIST
    (PMD) 92 2634 3741 90.00 14.49 6.13 14.2 ch tk
    (ex Roland Essberger-97)
EBRO (PRT) 86 2238 2898 81.01 14.03 5.53 12.5 ch tk
    (ex Eberhart Essberger-95)
LIMA CHEMIST
    (PMD) 92 2634 3750 90.00 14.49 6.15 14.0 ch tk
    (ex Liselotte Essberger-97)
RENO (PRT) 86 2238 2898 81.01 13.75 5.53 13.0 ch tk
    (ex Heinrich Essberger-94)

TEJO CHEMIST
      (PMD)   92   2634 3742   90.00 14.49   6.15 14.0 ch tk
  (ex John Augustus Essberger-97)
TOM ELBA (PRT)   80   1958 2544   80.88 13.42   5.13 12.2 ch tk
  (ex Helga Essberger-92)
TOM LIS (PRT)   80   1958 2544   80.88 13.42   5.13 12.2 ch tk
  (ex Liesel Essberger-92)

Blue Circle Financial Services Ltd. & Bamburi Tankers Holding Corp.
CEMENTIA (PAN)   67   3739 5335   106.61 15.55   6.74 14.7 cem
DALIA (PAN)   70   3739 5300   100.61 15.55   6.77 14.7 cem

Südsee Tank-Reederei GmbH
CHRISTIAN ESSBERGER
      (PRT)   00   3550 4710   99.90 15.40   6.55 15.0 ch tk

Chemical Tanker Services East Pte. Ltd.
CORAL ESSBERGER
      (SGP)   81   1941 2893   81.31 13.42   5.34 12.2 ch tk
ESSBERGER PIONEER
      (SGP)   75   1616 2456   77.12 12.60   5.20 12.0 ch tk
  (ex Alpha Lady-92, Ellen Essberger-86, Solvent Venturer-81, Essberger Pioneer-77)

Chemical Carriers East Pte. Ltd.
ESSBERGER PROGRESS
      (SGP)   81   3796 6162   108.34 16.01   6.83 13.5 ch tk
  (ex Golden Kyosei-96, Golden Kyosei Maru-91)

Karibik Tank-Reederei GmbH
PATRICIA ESSBERGER
      (PMD)   00   3550 4710   99.90 15.40   6.55 15.0 ch tk
Also larger ships.

TRITON BEREEDERUNGS GmbH & CO. KG

ANASTASIA (ATG)   84   1409 1545   79.00 10.93   3.30 10.0 gen(80c)
  (ex Nadja-01, Mari Claire-98, Kirsten-94)
SONJA (ATG)   84   1410 1562   79.00 10.93   3.31 10.5 gen(80c)
  (ex Desiree-01, Mari Line-98, Sea Ems-96)

Triton Schiffahrts GmbH & Co KG m.s. "Lebasee"
LEBASEE (DEU)   97   2528 3500   88.60 12.80   5.52 12.5 gen(167c)
  (ex Sao Vicente-97, Lebasee-97)

Triton Schiffahrts GmbH & Co KG m.s. "Mareike"
MAREIKE (ANT)   84   1843 2325   80.50 12.70   4.16 10.8 gen(102c)
  (ex Lys Coast-98, Erkaburg-91, Lys Coast-91, Erkaburg-91)

Triton Reefer Navigation Co. Ltd.
NORDER TILL (ATG) 86   1416 1550   79.02 11.61   3.30 10.0 gen(80c)
  (ex Triton-98, Mari France-96, Simone-94)

Triton Schiffahrts GmbH & Co KG m.s. "Triton Elbe"
TRITON ELBE (ATG) 88   910 1083   69.12   9.52   3.00 10.5 gen(36c)
  (ex Howden-99, Sea Danube-96)

Triton Schiffahrts GmbH & Co KG m.s. "Triton Loga"
TRITON LOGA
      (ANT)   87   2749 3173   94.52 16.16   4.99 14.0 gen(262c)
  (ex Jan Becker-98)
This company also manages several ships for Dutch companies.
Also larger ships.

UNITAS SCHIFFAHRTS GmbH & CO. KG

Unitas Schiffahrtsges. mbH m.s. "Ady" KG
ADY (ATG)   95   2899 3950   99.33 16.20   4.90 14.5 gen(340c)
(ex Bell Ady-97)
Unitas Schiffahrtsges. mbH & Co. m.s. "German" KG
GERMAN (DEU)   92   3585 4150   99.85 16.30   5.40 15.0 gen(325c)
(ex CMBT Challenge-97, Aquitaine Challenge-96, German-96, Gracechurch Star-95, German-94, Jork-93)
Unitas Schiffahrtsges. mbH & Co. m.s. "Iduna" KG
IDUNA (DEU)   91   3585 4150   98.80 16.30   5.40 14.6 gen(361c)
(ex CMB Iduna-95, Iduna-94)

VEGA-REEDEREI FRIEDRICH DAUBER KG

Partenreederei m.s. "Heidberg"
HEIDBERG (DEU)   85   1957 2892   87.97 11.54   4.66 11.0 gen(90c)
Partenreederei m.s. "Mühlenberg"
MÜHLENBERG
        (DEU)   86   1957 2886   87.86 11.54   4.67 11.0 gen(90c)
Minicargo Shipping Co. Ltd.
NORMANNIA (CYP)   83   1946 1395   87.97 11.54   4.68 11.0 gen(90c)
(ex Baursberg-97)
Arend Brugge m.s. "Polterberg" KG
POLTERBERG (DEU) 83   1945 2904   87.97 11.54   4.68 11.0 gen(90c)
Minibulk Shipping & Trading Ltd.
SPRÜTTENBERG
        (DEU)   81   2265 2870   99.83 11.41   4.30 10.5 gen(100c)
(ex Montania-01, Thekla-96, Clovis-88, Thekla Wessels-86)
Partenreederei m.s. "Süllberg"
SÜLLBERG (DEU)   94   1999 3280   90.28 12.58   4.64 11.0 gen(116c)
Partenreederei m.s. "Tafelberg"
TAFELBERG (DEU)   81   1939 2890   87.97 11.33   4.67 11.5 gen(90c)
(ex Helga-92)
Partenreederei m.s. "Waseberg"
WASEBERG (DEU)   85   1957 2890   87.97 11.31   4.66 11.0 gen(90c)

REEDEREI HEINZ-GEORG VÖGE KG

Partenreederei m.s. "Frieda" K.R. H-G. Vöge
FRIEDA (DEU)   93   3992 5336   99.50 18.44   6.55 15.3 gen(509c)
(ex Scandinavian Bridge-99, Frieda-93)
m.s. "Jan Fabian" Heinz-Georg Vöge
JAN-FABIAN (DEU) 97   3999 5210   99.95 18.20   6.56 15.5 cc(508c)
Partenreederei m.s. "Rita" Heinz-Georg Vöge
RITA (DEU)   95   3999 5314   101.11 18.45   6.55 15.5 gen(508c)
m.s. "Robert" Reederei H. G. Vöge KG
ROBERT (DEU)   83   3435 4188   98.66 15.47   5.51 14.0 gen(338c)
(ex CTE Istanbul-01, Robert-00, Rhein Partner-93, Robert-92, ECL Commander-92, Robert-91, Gracechurch Crown-86, Akak Success-84, Robert-84)
Also larger ships.

JAN VOGELSANG

Vogelsang-Bereederungs KG m.s. "Jan V"
JAN-V (DEU)   85   1749 2218   80.73 12.63   4.18 12.0 gen(142c)

ERNST-AUGUST VON ALLWÖRDEN

m.s. "Magda" Ernst-August von Allworden und Dirk Jager KG

MAGDA (DEU) 95 3999 5216 100.60 18.45 6.56 15.5 gen(509c)

m.s. "Berolin" Ernst-August von Allworden und Dirk Jager KG

RHEIN PARTNER

(ATG) 94 3992 5350 99.95 18.44 6.55 15.5 gen(509c)

(ex Berolin-98, UB Jaguar-97, Iberian Bridge-96, Berolin-94)

Also the larger JOANNA BORCHARD.

UWE VON ALLWÖRDEN KG

Tasman Shipping Co. Ltd.

ANDORRA (ATG) 84 2118 3042 92.11 11.54 4.70 11.0 gen(100c)

(ex Halina-97, Idun-89, Halina-88)

Uwe von Allworden KG m.s. "Hera"

HERA (DEU) 90 2606 3240 89.99 13.03 4.58 11.0 gen(198c)

m.s. "Sagitta" Schiffahrtsgesellschaft mbH & Co.

SAGITTA (DEU) 90 1985 2620 82.50 12.50 4.47 11.0 gen(98c)

(launched as Rosemarie)

HANS-HINRICH VON RÖNN

Hans-Hinrich von Rönn m.s. "Navigator" Schiffahrts KG

NAVIGATOR (ATG) 81 1811 2668 78.59 12.83 4.60 10.2 gen(88c)

HANS-MATTHÄUS VOSS

Partenreederei KR Hans-Matthaus Voss m.s. "Uppland"

UPPLAND (DEU) 84 3093 3185 95.51 15.24 4.40 12.0 gen(207c)

(ex Karin-92)

WARNHOLTZ, SCHMIDT UND CO.

"Boxship" H. P. Matthiesen KG

ALADIN (CYP) 82 1499 1766 82.48 11.38 3.54 10.5 gen(48c)

Hans-Peter Matthiesen & Co.

ALI BABA (CYP) 83 1518 1768 82.48 11.38 3.55 10.5 gen(48c)

SESAM (CYP) 81 1499 1768 82.48 11.38 3.54 10.5 gen(48c)

Matthiesen Schiffahrts KG

SINDBAD (CYP) 81 1499 1769 82.48 11.33 3.54 10.5 gen(48c)

WARNECKE SCHIFFAHRTS KG

m.s. "Suntis" Warnecke Schiffahrts KG

SUNTIS (DEU) 85 1564 1815 82.48 11.33 3.63 10.5 gen(48c)

OSKAR WEHR KG (GmbH & CO.)

Partenreederei m.s. "Jurgen Wehr"

THAMES STAR (TUV)74 3287 4020 106.63 14.53 4.86 14.5 gen(272c)

(ex Janne Wehr-95, Containerships I-87, Janne Wehr-85, Roxane Kersten-83,
Janne Wehr-82, Roxane Kersten-81, Janne Wehr-80)

Also larger ships.

UWE WERNER

KARINA W (DEU) 65 658 719 55.07 9.33 3.21 10.0 gen

(ex Adele Hagenah-89)

WESCO SHIPPING GmbH & Co. KG

m.s. "Express" WESCO Shipping GmbH & Co. KG
EXPRESS (ATG)   93   2514 3650   87.75 12.80   5.52 11.5 gen(168c)
(ex Seapride Spirit-98, Poel-97)
Rudiger Fleig Schiffahrts KG m.s. "Faust"
FAUST (DEU)   97   2997 4444   99.90 12.80   5.67 13.0 gen(297c)
(ex German Express-97)
m.s. "German Bay" WESCO Shipping & Co. KG
GERMAN BAY (ATG) 97   2997 4444   99.90 12.80   5.67 13.0 gen(297c)
m.s. "German Sky" WESCO Shipping GmbH & Co. KG
GERMAN SKY (ATG) 96   2997 4450   95.30 12.80   5.67 13.0 gen(300c)
(ex Dutch Sky-01, German Sky-97, Rhein Pilot-96, German Sky-96)
Friendly Waters Shipping Ltd.
GORKY (CYP)   97   2914 3387   96.30 13.60   5.16 10.7 gen
(ex Transworld I-00)
Reind Wessels
PASADENA (ATG)   98   2993 4250   90.23 15.20   5.64 12.3 gen
(ex Reind Wessels-01 launched as Prompt)
m.s. "German Feeder" WESCO Shipping GmbH & Co. KG
POET (DEU)   97   2997 4450   95.30 12.80   5.67 13.0 gen(300c)
(ex German Feeder-00)
Associated with River-Liner Befrachtungs- u. Bereederungs. GmbH (q.v.)

The **COMET** approaches the Maas anchorage on 25 June 1999.   (Barry Standerline)

SCHIFFAHRTSKONTOR REEDEREI GEBRÜDER WINTER

m.s. "Comet" Gebr. Winter Reedereiges. mbH & Co. KG
COMET (DEU)   98   3999 5215   99.95 18.20   6.65 15.5 cc(508c)
m.s. "Corsar" Gebr. Winter Reedereiges. mbH & Co. KG
CORSAR (DEU)   98   3999 5215   99.95 18.20   6.65 15.5 cc(508c)

Reederei m.s. "Corvette" Jakob Winter KG
CORVETTE   (ATG)   91   3815 4654   103.50   16.24   6.09 15.0 gen(374c)
(ex Portlink Corvette-01, CMBT Corvette-00, Corvette-94, Lloyd Scandinavia-92,
Dana Corvette-91, launched as Corvette)
Cosmopolitan Shipping Ltd
HMS GOODWILL
      (ATG)   85   3797 4570   96.98   17.84   5.96 14.7 gen(356c)
(ex Commodore Goodwill-95, Akak Cedar-87)
Reederei m.s. "Cimbria" Harald Winter KG
RHEIN CARRIER
      (ATG)   91   3815 4654   103.54   16.24   6.08 15.0 gen(374c)
(ex Churruca-98, Cimbria-93, Lloyd Iberia-92, Dana Sirena-91, launched as Cimbria)
Also larger ships

BERND WITTKOWSKI
m.s. "Neckar" Kapitan Bernd Wittkowski KG
SEA THAMES   (ATG) 85   1616 2280   82.48   11.38   3.80 10.5 gen(67c)
(ex Kurt Jensen-94)

SCHIFFAHRTSKONTOR TOM WÖRDEN GmbH
Balandria Shipping Co. Ltd.
ÅNGERMANLAND
      (IOM)   89   3845 4334   104.85   16.00   5.37 14.6 gen(320c)
MEDELPAD   (IOM)   85   2696 2934   92.51   13.85   4.48 11.5 gen(166c)
(ex Merlin-97)

The **MEDELPAD** enters the Kiel Canal on a sunny 5 March 2001 with a cargo of sawn timber
from Sundsvall for delivery to the French port of Rochefort.   (Oliver Sesemann)

Partenreederei m.s. "Dalarna"
DALARNA   (CYP)   96   3796 4400   100.70   16.20   4.75 11.0 gen(200c)
(ex Aurico I-97)

Partenreederei m.s. "Gästrikland"
GÄSTRIKLAND
     (IOM)   92   4090 4601   111.10 16.07   5.98 15.3 gen(357c)
    (ex Sea-Voyager-98, Gästrikland-96)
    Tom Wörden Verwaltungsgesellschaft mbH & Co. m.s. "Merino" KG
GRACECHURCH METEOR
     (ATG)   97   3999 5500   99.95 18.20   6.60 17.5 cc(523c)
    (completed as Merino)
    m.s. "Hälsingland" Klaus Wilhelm Tom Wörden KG
HÄLSINGLAND
     (IOM)   90   3845 3936   104.85 16.26   5.86 14.6 gen(326c)
    Partenreederei m.s. "Chopin"
JÄMTLAND (NLD)   92   4071 5685   104.40 16.20   6.40 14.0 gen(312c)
    (ex Chopin-97, Ville d'Autan-93, Chopin-92, Stella Adriatic-92, launched as Christina)
    Partenreederei m.s. "Öland"
ÖLAND (DEU)   85   1371 1520   75.01 10.80   3.71 11.0 gen
    (ex Drochtersen-98)
Newbuildings :
LIVLAND (CYP)   01   3000 4400   99.95 16.50   4.80 11.8 gen
SILVA (CYP)   01   3000 4400   99.95 16.50   4.80 11.8 gen
Also larger ships.

H. H. WÜBBE NACHFOLGER
    m.s. "Mars" Küstenmotorschiff Reederei Theilen-Fanselauthoms
LASS MARS (DEU) 92   1515 2386   74.94 11.40   4.35 11.0 gen
    (launched as Mars)
    m.s. "Moon" S.K.R. Küstenmotorschiffreederei GmbH & Co. KG
LASS MOON (DEU) 92   1512 2386   74.94 11.40   4.35 11.0 gen
    (ex Moon-92)
    m.s. "Neptun" S.K.R. Küstenmotorschiff-Reederei GmbH & Co. KG
LASS NEPTUN
     DEU)   92   1512 2366   74.94 11.40   4.35 11.0 gen
    (ex Wolgast-94, Lass Neptun-93, launched as Neptun)
    m.s. "Saturn" S.K.R. Küstenmotorschiff-Reederei GmbH & Co. KG
LASS SATURN
     (DEU)   93   1513 2366   74.94 11.40   4.35 11.0 gen
    (ex Greifswald-94, Lass Saturn-93)
    m.s. "Uranus" S.K.R. Küstenmotorschiff Reederei GmbH & Co. KG
LASS URANUS
     (DEU)   92   1512 2386   74.94 11.40   4.35 11.0 gen
    (launched as Uranus)

ZIRKEL VERWALTUNGSGESELLSCHAFT mbH
    Partenreederei m.s. "Tainui"
AMICA (ATG)   93   2400 3300   85.35 12.60   5.18 13.0 gen(231c)
    (ex Tainui-01)
    m.s. "Hunte" GmbH & Co. KG
HUNTE (ATG)   80   1710 1644   71.40 12.83   3.92 11.0 gen(130c)
    (ex Frey-90)
Also larger ships.

Key to flag abbreviations

ANT	Netherlands Antilles
ATG	Antigua & Barbuda
BHS	Bahamas
CPV	Cape Verde
CYP	Cyprus
DEU	Germany
GIB	Gibralter
HND	Honduras
IOM	Isle of Man
LBR	Liberia
LUX	Luxembourg
MAR	Morocco
MLT	Malta
NIS	Norwegian International Register
NLD	Netherlands
PAN	Panama
PMD	Madeira
PRT	Portugal
SGP	Singapore
TUV	Tuvalu
VCT	St. Vincent & Grenadines

Key to vessel type abbreviations

bulk	bulk carrier
cc(c)	container carrier (container capacity in 20-foot equivalent units (TEUs))
cem	bulk cement carrier
ch tk	chemical tanker
gen	general cargo
gen(c)	general cargo (container capacity in TEUs)
gen/pt	general cargo/palletised cargo
gen/ro	general cargo/RoRo facility
lpg	liquified gas tanker
oil/ch tk	oil/chemical tanker
ref	refrigerated cargo
tk	tanker

LATE NEWS...

The STADT WANGEN (page 13) has been laid up for sale at Krautsand since March 2001.

The ARNEB (page 35) has been sold to UK owners and arrived at Manchester on 25 July 2001 for conversionfor the carriage of cargoes associated with nuclear fuel reprocessing. It is reported that the ship will be renamed ATLANTIC OSPREY.

Additional Ship
Fresena Reederei m.s. "Millennium" GmbH & Co. KG
VALIDUS (ATG)   00   2990   4805   99.63   16.90   5.90 15.0 gen(370c)
(ex MILLENNIUM-01)

INDEX OF CURRENT SHIPS' NAMES

CORONA	24	ENNO B	10	GRANEBORG	20
CORONEL	60	ERIC HAMMANN	30	GRAUERORT	37
CORSAR	75	ERKA SUN	24	GRETA (1126gt/70)	57
CORVETTE	76	ESMERALDA	51	GRETA (2999gt/99)	51
COSA	25	ESSBERGER PIONEER	72	GRIMM	49
COSMEA	21	ESSBERGER PROGRESS	72	GROOTHUSEN	10
CRESCENT RHINE	56	EUKLID	56	GUADALUPE 2	64
CRESCENT SEINE	56	EVA MARIA MÜLLER	38	GUDRUN	28
DAKOTA	69	EVENBURG	53	GUDRUN II	50
DALARNA	76	EVERSMEER	53	HAI	27
DALIA	72	EVERT PRAHM	30	HAJO	21
DANIA (2691gt/85)	6	EWALD	48	HÄLSINGLAND	77
DANIA (2997gt/01)	51	EXPRESS	75	HAMBURG	40
DANIO	20	FALDERNTOR	53	HAMMELWARDEN	36
DEALER	66	FAUST	75	HAMPOEL	47
DEBORAH	11	FELIX	50	HANDORF	31
DELIA	68	FIGAROS	18	HANNA	3
DELTAGAS	64	FINJA	20	HANNES D	59
DENEB	48	FIONE	33	HANS LEHMANN	45
DENIKA	20	FLEVO	33	HANSE	16
DEVER	22	FLINTHÖRN	16	HANSEATIC SAILOR	31
DIDE	62	FLORA	48	HAUGO	33
DITHMARSIA	7	FORESTER (2827gt/90)	18	HEIDBERG	73
DITZUM	15	FORESTER (4110gt/96)	14	HEIDE	28
DOLLART	15	FRANCOP	6	HEIKE	61
DONIZETTI	27	FRANKO	20	HEIKE LEHMANN	45
DORADO	60	FREEPSUM	10	HEIKO B	10
DORIS T	21	FREJ	65	HEIMATLAND	16
DORNUM	10	FREYA	16	HEINRICH BEHRMANN	8
DOURO CHEMIST	71	FRIEDA (2901gt/96)	19	HELA	8
DRAX	25	FRIEDA (3992gt/93)	73	HELEN	46
DREDGER	66	FRIGGA	16	HELENA	51
DUISBURG	31	FUNDO	57	HELGA	50
DUNKERQUE EXPRESS II	40	GAMBLER	67	HELGOLAND	62
EASTWIND	4	GAMMAGAS	64	HELIOS II	57
EBBA	20	GARMO	33	HELJO	54
EBERHARD	52	GÄSTRIKLAND	77	HELLA	50
EBRO	71	GEEST ATLAS	60	HELSE	67
EDDA	19	GEEST MERCHANT	40	HELSINKI	12
EIDER	38	GEEST TRADER	40	HENNING S.	69
EILSUM	10	GEMINUS	48	HENNY	62
ELBE STAR	37	GERD SIBUM	64	HENRIETTE	31
ELBIA	57	GERDA	54	HERA (1202gt/75)	60
ELDOR	29	GERHARD K	40	HERA (2606gt/90)	74
ELISABETH (1139gt/83)	70	GERHARD PRAHM	30	HERMANN G	34
ELISABETH (2851gt/69)	33	GERHEIN G	27	HESTIA	68
ELISABETH (3958gt/93)	21	GERLENE	27	HMS GOODWILL	76
ELISIA	5	GERMAN	73	HMS PORTUGAL	50
ELKE (1299gt/84)	23	GERMAN BAY	75	HOHEWEG	54
ELKE (1473gt/86)	50	GERMAN SKY	75	HOLGER	69
ELSEBETH	67	GLOBAL POWER	53	HOLSATIA	7
ELVI KULL	45	GODEWIND	4	HOLSTEIN	65
EMILY	23	GOLF	54	HOMBERG	31
EMJA	13	GORCH FOCH	68	HUEMMLING	19
EMMA	50	GORKY	75	HUNTE	77
EMSLAND	46	GÖTALAND	47	HUNTER	67
EMSTAL	32	GRACECHURCH COMET	21	IBIZA	12
EMSTANK 7	24	GRACECHURCH CROWN	6	IDA RAMBOW	54
EMSTANK 10	24	GRACECHURCH HARP	21	IDUNA	73
EMSTOR	53	GRACECHURCH METEOR	77	ILKA	70

INCA	69	KITE	4	MARIANNE (1934gt/78)	35
INDUSTRIAL ACCORD	16	KOMET III	27	MARIANNE (2765gt/74)	28
INDUSTRIAL BEACON	54	KOPENHAGEN	12	MARIE LEHMANN	46
INDUSTRIAL CARIBE	16	KOPERSAND	17	MARIE-THERESE	32
INGA	38	KORALLE	67	MARILENA	25
INGO J.	37	KORMORAN	37	MARIS	48
INGRID	27	KORSIKA	12	MARJESCO	29
INNES	25	KRONOBORG	25	MARLIES SABBAN	60
IRIS-JÖRG	39	KYLEMORE	25	MARLIN	64
IRLO	59	LA ROCHELLE EXPRESS	40	MARMAN	21
IRMGARD	70	LADY BOS	18	MARSCHENLAND	17
ISABELLA	51	LAILA	18	MARTHA HAMMANN	30
ISARTAL	33	LARA	51	MATHILDA	21
ISEBEK	40	LARGO II	59	MCL EXPRESS	57
JACARANDA	12	LARGONA	59	MEDELPAD	76
JACOB BECKER	8	LARK	18	MEDITERRANEO	29
JAMAL	70	LASBEK	40	MEKONG FORTUNE	52
JAMBO	34	LASS MARS	77	MEKONG PIONEER	37
JÄMTLAND	77	LASS MOON	77	MELANIE Z	57
JAN-FABIAN	73	LASS NEPTUN	77	MELISSA	25
JAN-RASMUS	6	LASS SATURN	77	MELODY	51
JAN-V	73	LASS URANUS	77	MEMEL	13
JAN-WILLEM	23	LAURA	32	MERIT	63
JANE	33	LAURA HELENA	33	MERKUR	6
JANRA	51	LEA	10	MERLE	28
JENNA CATHERINE	38	LEBASEE	72	MERMAID	63
JENS R	10	LEESWIG	47	MERWEGAS	64
JEROME H.	68	LENNARD	34	MICHELLE	35
JERSBEK	40	LEONA	38	MIGNON	4
JESSICA	59	LIMA	69	MIKA	27
JO CURACAO	47	LIMA CHEMIST	71	MIKE	67
JOHANN	12	LINACO	71	MINCHEN D	59
JOHN C. HELMSING	33	LINDA BUCK	18	MIRAMAR	17
JOLANDA	59	LINGEGAS	64	MIRIAM	21
JONAS	19	LISA LEHMANN	46	MISTRAL	59
JORUND	65	LIVLAND	77	MOLDAVIA	57
JULIA ISABEL	28	LORE PRAHM	30	MONA ROSA	71
JUMPER	67	LUCAS	28	MONIKA MÜLLER	38
JUPITER	32	LUCKY	45	MONTE VERDE	50
JUTTA-B	14	LYDIA	35	MOZART	27
KAAKSBURG	63	LYDIA B	10	MSC BAHAMAS	68
KABAN	71	LYS CARRIER	22	MÜHLENBERG	73
KAJA-H	34	LYS CHRIS	33	MULTITANK BADENIA	3
KAJEN	49	LYS CLIPPER	23	MULTITANK BAHIA	3
KAMILLA	22	MAGDA	74	MULTITANK BALEARIA	3
KARIN	48	MAGULA	20	MULTITANK BATAVIA	47
KARIN LEHMANN	46	MAIKE	70	MULTITANK BOLOGNIA	3
KARINA W	74	MAJA-M	55	MULTITANK BRACARIA	3
KATHARINA B	61	MALANGA	71	MULTITANK BRASILIA	3
KATHARINA D	7	MALLORCA	12	MULTITANK BRITANNIA	3
KATHARINA EHLER	23	MALTE B	10	MULTITANK CALABRIA	3
KATHARINA SIEMER	64	MANYA	48	MULTITANK IBERIA	47
KATRIN	20	MARCEL	68	MÜNSTER	32
KAY L.	68	MAREK	67	MURRAY	26
KELLS	25	MAREIKE	72	MUSKETIER	17
KERSTIN	53	MARGARETA	18	NADINE	32
KIEFERNWALD	4	MARGARETA B	61	NANDIA	45
KILLARNEY	25	MARIA D	7	NATALIE	62
KIMBERLEY	16	MARIA H	57	NAUTILA	28
KIRSTEN	50	MARIANN	33	NAVIGATOR	74

NAVIGIA	70	PARMA	57	RHEINFELS	59
NEERLANDIC	70	PARSIVAL	57	RHEINTAL	32
NEERMOOR	13	PASADENA (1599gt/01)	58	RHINE-LINER	63
NEMUNA	57	PASADENA (2993gt/01)	75	RIA	36
NENUFAR EUROPE	50	PASSATWIND	4	RICHARD C	69
NERVA	8	PATRIA	35	RIGA	13
NESS	54	PATRICIA ESSBERGER	72	RIJA	3
NESSE	53	PATRIOT	35	RIKA	48
NESSERLAND	17	PAUL	52	RIO-Y-MAR	48
NESTOR	69	PAULA	14	RITA	73
NEUENBROK	13	PEARY	58	RIVER ALN	21
NEULAND	62	PEGASUS	13	RIVER BLYTH	22
NEUWERK	17	PEIKKO	35	RIVER TYNE	22
NICOLA	35	PERA	58	RMS ALDEBARAN	23
NIEDERELBE	54	PERFORMER	67	RMS ANDROMEDA	23
NIKAR G	27	PERLE	58	RMS ARCTURUS	24
NIKLAS	46	PERU	58	RMS DUISBURG	55
NILS B	10	PETERSBURG	63	RMS LAGUNE	67
NINA	47	PETRA	36	RMS MULHEIM	55
NINCOP	6	PETRA F.	24	RMS RUHRORT	56
NOORT	19	PEX	58	RMS VOERDE	56
NORDER TILL	72	PHANTOM	35	RMS WALSUM	56
NORDERFELD	6	PHILIPP	28	RMS WESTFALIA	67
NORDERTOR	35	PIA (2236gt/87)	27	ROBERT	73
NORDICA	49	PIA (1720gt/85)	64	ROGER	67
NORDLAND I	62	PINTA	35	ROLF BUCK	18
NORDSEE	37	PIONIER	35	ROSA	51
NORDSTERN	57	PLANET V	27	ROSSINI	27
NORDSTRAND	35	PLATO	34	RUTH	19
NORDWIND	37	PLUS	58	RUTH-W	6
NORMANNIA	73	PODEDRADY	58	RYSUM	10
NORMED ISTANBUL	60	POET	75	S. GABRIEL	17
NORRLAND	51	POLA	58	SAGITTA	74
NORTHSEA TRADER	19	POLARWIND	4	SAGITTA J.	38
NOUMEA EXPRESS	46	POLTERBERG	73	SALAMANDER	26
NYLAND	36	POMMERN	58	SANDFELD	6
ODIN	65	PORTHOS	17	SANDRA	36
OKAPI	26	PORTLINK CARAVEL	50	SANDWATER	53
OLAF J.	36	POSEN	58	SANTA MARIA	47
ÖLAND	77	POTOSI	59	SANTIAGO	17
OLIVIA	19	PRÄSIDENT	59	SARAH	50
OMEGAGAS	64	PREMIERE	35	SARDINIA	13
ORADE	20	PRIWALL	39	SATURN	69
ORION	13	PROGRESO	17	SAXUM	17
ORSO	10	PROTEUS	35	SCHARHÖRN	17
ORTRUD	55	PROVIDER	67	SCHULENBURG	63
OSLO	13	PUCCINI	27	SCOTIA	50
OSTERHUSEN	10	PYRGOS	26	SCOUT MARIN	48
OSTWIND	4	RADESFORDE	47	SEA CLYDE	23
OTTAR	7	RAMBLER	48	SEA EMS	60
OTTO BECKER	8	RANGITANE	46	SEA MERSEY	17
P & O NEDLLOYD GIZAN	70	REBECCA HAMMANN	30	SEA THAMES	76
P & O NEDLLOYD OBOCK	37	REGINA J.	38	SEA WAAL	60
P & O NEDLLOYD TRINIDAD	38	REMORA	20	SEABOARD ENDEAVOUR	13
PAASCHBURG	63	RENATE	62	SEABOARD SPIRIT	38
PAHNA	32	RENO	71	SEEBRISE	4
PALUCCA	32	RHEIN CARRIER	76	SELENE PRAHM	30
PAMELA	35	RHEIN MASTER	32	SESAM	74
PAMIR	57	RHEIN PARTNER	74	SHEILA HAMMANN	30
PARAMAR	32	RHEIN TRADER	39	SIAN	26

Cover illustrations

Front cover : The **RADESFORDE** was photographed as she arrived at Sharpness on a sunny 19 August 1999 to discharge 2800 tonnes of fertiliser from Szczecin.

(Bernard McCall)

Back cover : There is much fascination to be derived from the ever-changing shipping scene and the following of ship histories. The **HEMO** now trades as **KEVIN S**, as noted on page 39. She makes a fine sight as she sails down the River Elbe on 30 May 2000.

(Bernard McCall)

The **PHILIPP** is usually to be found linking Rotterdam to Felixstowe, Grangemouth and the River Tyne. On 19 October 1998 she was photographed arriving off the port of Blyth where she made occasional calls during that year. (Nigel J Cutts)

A fine view of the **NEERMOOR** as she approaches Swansea in the morning light of 19 June 1996. She loaded steel coils for the Spanish port of Sagunto.

(Bill Moore, courtesy ABP Swansea)